DIABETIC
TRAVEL TALES and TIPS

Adventures from Around the World

MARILYN L. GARCIA
AND OTHER DIABETIC TRAVELERS

MANDEAN
PRESS

10 9 8 7 6 5 4 3 2 1

Library of Congress Control Number: 2005902340

Published by Mandean Press
P.O Box 93452
Pasadena, Ca 91109
www.diabetictraveltales.com

Bulk purchases of *Diabetic Travel Tales and Tips* are available to
companies, organizations, nonprofits and others at special discounts. For
more information, go to www.diabetictraveltales.com.

Reasonable steps have been taken to confirm the accuracy of the
information in this book, but the safety, efficacy and applicability of
any recommendation cannot be guaranteed, and may not be appropriate in particular cases. Individuals should consult a physician or other
health care professional before undertaking any recommendation in
this book. Information in *Diabetic Travel Tales and Tips* was obtained
from sources believed to be reliable at the time of publication, but
such information may not be complete and may need to be updated in
the future. No compensation or favors were received to include any
information or products in this book.

   Diabetic Travel Tales and Tips is not intended to give comprehensive
advice about diabetes care or self-management, or to provide complete information necessary for travel.

Book and cover design: Stefan Gutermuth
Illustrations by Elizabeth Kee

A portion of the sale proceeds from *Diabetic Travel Tales and Tips* will be
donated to nonprofit organizations and designated to be used to find a cure
for diabetes. For more information, go to www.diabetictraveltales.com.

TABLE OF CONTENTS

PART II   TIPS

PART III
ADDITIONAL INFORMATION

INTRODUCTION

Experience is the name so many people give to their mistakes.—Oscar Wilde

A few years ago I was in a crowded passenger lounge at San Jose International Airport during the Silicon Valley boom years when I observed two women—both blond, very attractive, probably in their mid-thirties—talking. One was extolling the virtues of her insulin pump to the other, and I realized both were insulin dependent diabetics. I have been an insulin dependent diabetic for many years. I mused how amazing it was that there were three insulin dependent diabetics, traveling without apparent problem, in such proximity. The women talked for a long time before I leaned over to one and whispered that I had been a diabetic for over 40 years. She immediately shouted so that everyone in the lounge could hear: "She has been a diabetic for over 40 years!" I was devastated and thought, "I wish she hadn't said that. I don't want people to think I am even that old."

There are over 18 million people with diabetes in the United States. Almost 6 million take insulin, either by injection or an insulin pump. Another 10 million take only oral medication to control their diabetes. With the time changes, foreign languages and varied cultures, travel can be difficult for diabetics who must rely on regular schedules for meals and medications. Contributors to *Diabetic Travel Tales and Tips* have taken international trips to countries in Europe, Asia, Africa and South America. I have encountered problems, many my own doing; others whose stories are included here have been incredibly successful under dire circumstances.

This book is about real life experiences and misadventures, and suggestions about how to avoid and survive problems. Part I contains true stories by diabetics and a doctor. Part II contains suggestions about how to deal with the problems encountered in each story. Part III contains additional useful information, including definitions of the diabetic words used in the stories.

This book is for diabetic travelers to enjoy and compare notes—you might discover you have been more successful than we have been in avoiding difficulties. It is also for new diabetics and those who have not yet traveled, and for the families of diabetics, who often worry more about us than we do ourselves. I hope the stories will impart the attitude, courage and luck necessary for travel, in addition to the tips and information.

Medical advances occur constantly. New medications and gadgets to make our lives easier come out regularly, and occasionally the rules change. The stories show how even the types of insulin have changed over the years. The suggestions are easy and practical ones to apply even as things improve.

Recently I learned that some people with diabetes prefer not to be called diabetics, the term used in this book and which I have used to describe myself for many years. To such people, I apologize. Please let actions speak louder than words. The active lives of the diabetics here, who don't mind this term, should be the true testament to living well with diabetes.

Bon voyage, and remember:

"If I look like this, I need the trip."
—Gloria Swanson (of her passport photo)

PART
ONE

TALES

ONE

THE FIRST BIG TRIP

by Marilyn L. Garcia

Never look down to test the ground before taking your next step; only he who keeps his eyes fixed on the far horizon will find his right road. —Dag Hammarskjöld

I n 1993 the Pan Pacific and Southeast Asian Women's Association selected me as one of three United States representatives to attend a seminar on the environment in Taipei, Taiwan. Other than Mexico, I had not traveled out of the country and I would be going by myself. The trip to Taiwan would require a drastic change in my insulin schedule to adjust to the time on the other side of the world. In the years since that first journey, these trans-Atlantic and trans-Pacific insulin adjustments have best defined my travel—fundamental changes easily mastered as one goes out into the world.

Even for that first trip, I was not intimidated, only excited. I had always wanted to go to Hong Kong—the shopping capital of the world—and hoped to include a foolishly expensive side trip there.

Then, only 10 days before I would leave and despite having seen my doctor well in advance of the trip, I ended up in the hospital, sick as a dog. But that turn of events did not stop me—I checked out of the hospital two days later, fully adjusted to the insulin regime, and one week after that I was off to the Far East by myself. Having diligently packed my medical supplies, and armed with a schedule for a 15-hour time zone transformation, I departed early one Saturday morning from Los Angeles for Seattle, then took an afternoon flight to Seoul, South Korea—taking an additional dose of intermediate-acting NPH during the 13-hour flight and some Regular insulin each time I ate—and arrived there well into the next day. I paced the length of the Seoul airport terminal to absorb the blinding sunlight that dominated the terminal windows, the essential antidote to adjust to the new time.

I arrived in Taipei on a muggy Sunday evening at

the Palace Hotel, the grand old hotel of Taiwan, hidden among lush grounds on an authoritative hill overlooking the city. As I disembarked from the cab, my eyeglasses fogged up from the August humidity, but the Palace Hotel welcomed me with appropriate grandeur for my first trip to the Far East: a cavernous lobby with ceilings so high I could not see them, massive red columns throughout the lobby, and a grand staircase leading up to the check-in desk. The hotel's narrow halls, thick plaster walls, dark moldings and severe room doors, evoked a bygone era. Perhaps because of its complex ties to the past, the hotel burned down a few years ago, apparently the result of arson committed by political dissidents.

When I tested my blood sugar in the room, it was 90—perfect!!—after a 20-hour trip, three airplane flights and a 15-hour time change.

Women from Fiji, the Marshall Islands, Palau, Japan, Malaysia, Guam, Taiwan, Hong Kong, Thailand, Korea, Indonesia, Canada, Mexico, Peru, South Africa and the United States attended the seminar. Women with diamond necklaces fit for the Queen of England, women in fine Malaysian silk saris, khaki-garbed women who had flown in from the jungles of Indonesia, mixed and mingled. There were the requisite ceremonial welcomes and dinners—where I discovered that Chinese noodles, while looking like vegetables, are very high in carbohydrates. My blood sugar shot through the roof until

I figured out how to adjust my insulin doses to cover the noodles.

Seminar speakers held forth on sustainable development and environmental education, positing such head-spinning ideas as: "Taking a global view, making the woman-nature affinity the theoretical grounding of ecofeminism appears to be problematic." Meaning that desperately poor women often kill trees to survive.

Then Hong Kong beckoned. Its density, merely an abstraction to me before then, unfolded as we descended into the Hong Kong airport over turquoise water, between skyscraper forests. The density hit again as I deplaned: orderly rectangles of hundreds of people waited for taxicabs. At last it was my turn, and the taxicab took me to the Kowloon Hotel, a glistening high rise across the street from the venerable Peninsula hotel in Kowloon, across the bay from Hong Kong. I planned to frequent the Peninsula for breakfast and afternoon tea, but not pay the premium to sleep there.

The next morning I was at the Peninsula for breakfast. The hotel was built in the 1920's, and I experienced a flashback to the colonial elegance of that time. Bellhops strolled through the room ringing little bells and carrying elegant paper signs to summon particular hotel guests. My table was covered with a linen table cloth and set with silver, so in the spirit of the setting, I ordered porridge, something I had only read about in children's books. Breakfast arrived in china and silver service; at that point I discovered porridge was oatmeal.

Then I set out to explore Kowloon. The city overwhelmed me with its capitalist confusion. Neon signs in incomprehensible Cantonese dominated narrow streets. The shops were so tightly packed I couldn't locate one even when I had its address. The shops offered all kinds of merchandise, from global generic to funky to downright cheap. But as a terrible bargainer, I gave up, joined the international jet set, and went to a "Hong Kong tailor" in the hotel arcade.

Surrounded by bolts of fine silks and woolen cloth, a stylish, graceful man first showed me a book of suit designs, then a book listing his clients from all over the world, and persuaded me to buy a suit. I selected a style and a fabric, his assistant measured me, and they told me to show up two days later for a final fitting. When I returned, the basic suit was done and the final product arrived at my house in California about the time I did.

Then two days into my visit, the hotel issued an ominous warning:

> "Typhoon signal number 8 was hoisted at 4.00pm today as Severe Tropical Storm Tasha is approaching and is expected to be closest to Hong Kong at 5.00am tomorrow morning."

Shops boarded their windows. The hotel ordered us to close our drapes to keep out shattering glass. Sheets of water slashed the building through the night. In the morning, the news reported several people had died. But later that day, with less than 24 hours remaining in my visit, I left the hotel in the still rainy weather, lured by one last shopping opportunity. The legendary Star ferry was not operating in the choppy sea, so I took the subway under the bay from Kowloon to Hong Kong proper for one last binge.

My journey home was even more arduous than the journey to Taiwan: first, a flight from Hong Kong back to Taiwan, then a 4-hour flight through the vast Pacific darkness to Guam, where, arriving at midnight, we were sprayed with insect repellant before deplaning. I spent the remainder of the night in the stifling Guam airport—on a bench. The airport lunch counter kept its only refreshments, soda cans, on the back shelf. It was a long way from porridge at the Peninsula.

Eventually our plane left Guam on a 7-hour flight to Honolulu, followed by a 5-hour flight home to Los Angeles. I learned a great deal on that first trip: the Pacific Ocean is very big, and I had crossed it and survived.

TWO

WILD IN CALIFORNIA

by Denise Little

*When I'm good, I'm very good, but when I'm bad,
I'm better.*—Mae West

Traveling as a type-1 diabetic is always a bit
disconcerting. But I'm blessed with a job I
love, and traveling is an essential part of that
job, so I'm generally in an airport line at least twice a
month. In all that traveling, I've learned some hard
lessons. I observe all the standard rules when I travel,
which are simply common sense. But even obses-

sively preparing for every trip can't prevent surprises. In my years of traveling as a diabetic, I've had my share of adventures.

Getting through security at airports is always exciting. Trying to explain a mass of syringes to stone-faced guards who are determined to believe that I'm a heroin addict or about to inject some nameless poison into their flight crews has become commonplace. So has trying to explain why they can't put my insulin pump through the X-ray machine unless I'm attached to it. I'm always patted down—and I've been strip searched once. I've learned to allow at least an extra two hours before my flight for tie-ups at security—and to expect to have to explain anything and everything I've got in my medical bag of tricks.

So far, over hundreds of trips, I've managed to get myself and my pump and my medicine bag through security every time—but it's rarely been without some kind of show-and-tell episode. I've learned to announce that I am a diabetic, and that my supplies are in this bag, as I put it on the belt for the X-ray machines. At least then the screeners have some form of advance notice to explain what they are looking at.

But just because they know doesn't mean that they'll approve. Screeners have a level of professional paranoia that makes sense after 9/11. But I've found that asking to see their supervisor in a calm, friendly voice after things start looking grim can usually get my situation unjammed.

After I've gone through security, the next bit of excitement is getting my carry-on on the plane. With the advent of regional jets, I have discovered that an airline-approved carry-on bag won't always fit on the plane. So I keep a small, zippered pocket bag of essentials for a single day inside my carry-on. That way, if the airline insists on gate-checking my bag, I can pull out the mini-kit for the plane flight before the flight attendant grabs my medical lifeline and throws it in the luggage hold.

I also pack a small food pack—that's as important as the medical supplies on most flights. I stock it with a sandwich, a piece of fruit, a pouch of tuna, and a bottle of water, at a bare minimum. If the weather looks chancy, I double or triple the provisions. That way, if I get stuck on the end of a runway on a ground hold or if the plane is delayed by mechanical difficulties, or if any of the other uncountable problems that airplanes can have crop up to keep me trapped in the plane long after I expected to be at my destination, I can eat at my scheduled time.

I once got stuck on the Detroit airport runway in a plane in a blinding snowstorm for eight hours. I was the only person on the plane who'd packed enough food and water to get through the flight without discomfort. Not only that, I was able to feed the folks around me—which made waiting for rescue a lot more pleasant.

But flight delays and security issues fall into the area of expected difficulties. I can prepare for those things. It's the unexpected troubles that require real flexibility.

One of my favorite stories about traveling as a diabetic occurred over a long Labor Day weekend. I was attending a convention in California. As always, I'd packed lots of supplies. I'd made sure that my insulin pump had a full load of insulin, and I'd replaced the battery before the trip, just in case. I carried a couple of spare batteries, as well. My pump, a D-Tron Plus, uses specialized long-lasting batteries that can only be acquired through the company that makes the pump—Disetronic. So it's essential that I pack spare batteries, because I can't just pick them up at a local pharmacy. For the record, I love my pump. It's truly completely waterproof, which is great for me because I do a lot of swimming. But having to have specialized batteries makes it necessary to plan ahead.

So does my job. I had a number of very important business meetings scheduled at this convention. I'd done my homework, and I was well prepared for the meetings. But, Murphy's Law being what it is, halfway through the weekend, at one of those meetings, I had a diabetic moment rear its ugly head.

I was the only woman at this meeting, and I was

wearing a silk business suit. Women's suits only rarely have a convenient place to put an insulin pump. I solved that problem the way I usually do— by stuffing my pump in my bra. I'm well endowed, and the pump is unnoticeable there under normal circumstances. But that meeting wasn't normal. About an hour into the meeting, my pump, for no apparent reason, decided that it was low on power. Never mind that I'd put in a new battery designed to last for a month only two days previously. The pump was deeply convinced that it was out of juice, and it was determined to let me—and everybody else in that meeting—know it. So, there in the middle of a roomful of men in suits, my chest suddenly started vibrating violently and making beeping noises. The first Austin Powers movie had just been released on video, and I could see the men recoil in shock and terror with visions of "fembots" darting through their brains.

I explained what was happening and excused myself. I had a spare battery in my purse, and I replaced the pump's power pack. I came back to the meeting, but for some reason, all of the men still looked uncomfortable. I guess they weren't expecting vibrating breasts in a business meeting. For what it's worth, neither was I! The meeting wound down, and I headed back to my hotel room. On the way, my pump alarm went off again, much to the surprise of the cabbie. And me. Once again, the pump was indicating it was out of power.

I had another battery in my luggage, and I put it in, but it was clear by now that something was desperately wrong. Even though it was a holiday weekend, I knew that my pump supplier maintained a twenty-four hour hotline. I called the number and explained my predicament. It turned out that my last supply shipment had been pulled from a bad batch of batteries—the company was about to recall them. The pump company offered to FedEx some new batteries to me at no charge, but given the holidays, the earliest that I could get the package was the following Tuesday.

That was of no use to me—I was stuck in California at a business convention on a holiday weekend, and my pump wasn't working. And I was leaving on Tuesday for home—assuming I could live that long.

Then the pump company offered to have their California rep drive to my hotel with replacement batteries the next day. That offer was a lifesaver, literally.

Pump insulin is fast acting, and it was all the insulin I had with me. While I had sufficient syringes packed in my luggage to keep myself alive by shooting up with my packed Humalog every hour or so, I couldn't go to sleep until I either got some long-acting insulin (impossible on that holiday weekend), or I got my pump back in action. Luckily, the new, functional batteries arrived just as promised. I got through the rest of the convention without another pump meltdown, and my life went back to normal.

Since then I've stockpiled batteries, and made sure that the ones I carry on trips come from multiple batches.

My convention disaster had its good side—the men I met that day remember me vividly. We still laugh about it. And we finalized the deal we discussed at that meeting.

THREE

SLEEPING AROUND

by Denise Little

Sleep faster, we need the pillows.
—Jewish proverb

This isn't exactly what it sounds like. No sexual hi-jinks. No thrilling adventures with members of the opposite sex.

At least, not exactly.

But, as a diabetic who travels a lot on business and for pleasure, I've had some wild adventures when I'm not sleeping in my own bed.

Luckily, I've never had any nocturnal diabetic adventures that required the presence of medics. Yet. One of the problems of traveling as a diabetic is that jet lag and unaccustomed activities can have a really nasty impact on routines that work well at home. I have a lot of diabetic friends, and I know more than one who has spent the night in the emergency room on a trip when blood sugars got way, way out of control. For someone with a job to do or serious pleasure to pursue in a new town, that can be a real downer.

So I'm thankful that my nocturnal adventures have been ER-free. But my trips haven't been without their share of night-time dramas.

One of the funniest adventures I've had was when I went home for Christmas a few years back. I have several nieces and nephews, and they all think that I'm simply splendid. And my siblings love having a night off. So I frequently end up spending the night after Christmas in Houston, Texas, overseeing a small crowd of children. Being something of an insomniac, what I'd do when bedtime got close was to build a giant sleeping bag out of blankets and pillows in front of the family room television, and we all would climb in and watch kids' movies until the last stubborn holdout child fell asleep. Then I'd carry them all to bed.

That system worked for several years. Until I got a delightful niece who needed even less sleep than I did. Not only that, this niece was exceptionally bright and fascinated by how things worked. Her experiments with electricity and tool use had kept her parents in a constant state of severe anxiety since the day she learned to walk at the age of seven months. The Christmas she nearly killed me she was three.

It was well past the wee hours in the morning, and she still hadn't fallen asleep yet. I knew when it was because I checked the time by using the Indi-Glo feature of my insulin pump to see how late it was. My niece was fascinated. I should have known better. But I just tucked her back in the bed and looked for another video.

We'd watched Disney films and National Velvet and Rugrats and Veggietales, and she still wasn't tired. I, on the other hand, was about to fall over. So I finally resorted to the ultimate weapon. I got out the Barney tapes, found the longest one, and put it on.

My niece immediately turned into a Barney Zombie. Try as I might to stay awake, I fell asleep to the treble voices of children singing to the purple dinosaur. An hour later, as the sun was coming up and I was dead to the world, the tape ran out. My niece, still wide awake, looked around for something to entertain herself with. She remembered my pump. It looked, she said later, just like a Nintendo controller. Even better, it lit up. And she wondered if she could turn its light on, and then use it like a remote control to get me out of bed and play with her. With her tiny little clever fingers, she gave it a good college try.

Luckily, I woke up before the insulin bolus took effect.

So I learned to hide my pump if I planned to sleep anywhere where inquisitive small children lived.

But children aren't the only problem factors in sleeping with an insulin pump as a guest in other people's homes. I've had a couple of pet disasters, too. Cats, in particular, can be quite insistent on fig-uring out what that pump is doing stuck to a human. At one friend's home, her pet cat crawled into bed with me during the night and carefully bit the tubing of the infusion set into several pieces. I woke up when I felt that the mattress was a little damp. I was worried that I'd somehow caused a problem on my friend's bedding. I had—but not in the way I'd feared. I'd just managed to drain 25 mL of insulin out of the severed tubing. Luckily I had a spare infusion set with me, and was able to solve the problem before any harm was done.

Another time, I had a friend's cat sleep next to me for most of the night. It didn't occur to me until my blood sugar kept rising and rising that a cat's body temperature is much higher than a human's. A normal healthy cat can have a body temperature ranging from 100 to 102.5 degrees Farenheit. The cat had slept on my insulin pump long enough to raise the temperature inside the cartridge and kill the insulin. I had to replace the cartridge.

Finally, I had a terrier attempt to grab my insulin pump and run off with it. But by this time, I'd learned my lesson about sleeping around in strange places with an insulin pump. It was duct taped to me. All the dog got for his efforts was sticky teeth and a big surprise.

FOUR

WE CAN'T SPEAK FRENCH

by Marilyn L. Garcia

In Paris they simply stared when I spoke to them in French; I never did succeed in making those idiots understand their own language. —Mark Twain

I t began with my doctor's remark, "If you have to buy insulin in France, it's all U-40, not the U-100 we have here, so you'll have to buy U-40 syringes too." U-40, U-80, U-100 – insulin concentrations. It reminded me of the many ways diabetes care had changed over the years. I had taken U-80 insulin many years ago—in glass syringes with stainless steel needles. But during this trip I couldn't imagine having to purchase insulin; I would pack two sets of medical supplies, one in my husband's carry-on brief case, the other in my purse.

I was thrilled to go to Paris, accompanying my husband, Arnoldo, on a business trip. Our two lucky children, Briana, who was then nine, and Marco, who was eight, would go too. Arriving in late June, we were confronted with cold and rain, and substituted our Southern California summer clothes with gray sweatshirts and jeans, blending in with the urban masses.

While Arnoldo attended business meetings, the children and I explored a city where none of us spoke the language. But Marco and Briana were not intimidated by the aloof, hurried Parisians and they concocted a way to handle them. As we walked down the street, they would stride forward, refusing to veer off course when strangers walked toward them. The children usually prevailed, causing their unknowing adversaries to walk around them.

"I won't go to the Louvre!" Marco exclaimed. He had adopted a policy of refusing to go to art museums on vacation trips. Later he begged to go to the Louvre upon learning that it contained paintings of beheaded saints and kings, flayed heroes and drowning sailors, and statues by Michelangelo, who, the story goes, carved and buried one in an attempt to pass it off as an antiquity.

I decided we would take a cab to the Pompidou Center to see modern art, then walk to the Marais, a warren of Renaissance buildings in the old Jewish quarter which was becoming gentrified with shops, art galleries and gay life. The day was a series of discombobulated efforts. The Pompidou Center was closed that day. The vast, inclined area in front was not inviting to us, and the Center itself—a steel frame that looked like scaffolding, glass walls, primary colors, and a tubed elevator crossing up its façade—was a shocking structure that didn't fit in Paris. Then we made our way down unfamiliar streets to the Marais, wandering among its shops and courtyards, cafes, turreted buildings and alleys. By mid-afternoon, it began to rain. Exhausted and disoriented, we took a cab back to the hotel.

At dinner time I looked in my purse for my insulin pack and discovered it wasn't there. It must have fallen out when we were getting out of the cab. Frantic, I searched the hotel room—the suitcases, the bathroom—for the backup insulin, but came up empty handed. That insulin must have been in my husband's briefcase, and he was gone. Then I remembered my doctor's advice, surprised that I would need to use it. I realized I was on my own. My doctor's comment merely informed me I didn't know enough to solve the problem by myself. Somehow I had to figure out what kinds of insulin to buy and purchase syringes to match the U-40 insulin sold in

France. To make matters worse, it was the July 4th weekend in the United States, and there was a 9-hour time difference. I called my doctor to get help, but it was impossible to reach him.

I found Arnoldo by telephone, at least, and he arranged for a doctor to speak with me. The doctor was one of the people with whom my husband was having business meetings. The doctor was not a diabetic specialist, so he consulted a manual and, in broken English that was better than my non-existent French, identified the types of insulin with the same acting durations as the short-acting Regular and the intermediate-acting NPH I took. *Voila!* I'd managed to get the information I needed. Taking two exhausted and protesting children by the hands, I made my way out of the hotel and down the street to find a pharmacy.

Somewhat uncertain what a pharmacy would even look like, we walked along crowded streets lined with formal gray buildings as it began to get dark and rain. Spotting a green neon cross sticking out of a wall high above us, we entered a brightly-lit room of glass cases and shelves full of unfamiliar boxes and bottles. A man in a white coat greeted us. My note with the types of insulin I needed was sufficient to communicate with the pharmacist. Then I gestured that I also needed syringes, and he easily produced them.

I didn't have any trouble persuading the pharmacist to sell me the insulin and syringes. Perhaps this was typical, or maybe I was so earnest and desperate he could not refuse. The most disconcerting thing of all was that the syringes I purchased had needles larger than the ones I had brought from the States.

Triumphant, I made my way back to the hotel with the children and took the new insulin, bigger needles and all. I was fine until my husband returned the next day with the backup medicine in his briefcase, and gladly switched to my regular stuff. This incident was the first of several during subsequent trips when I had to deal with being a diabetic in unfamiliar circumstances. I learned that with a little luck, problems could be solved.

FIVE

GOOD KARMA

by Catherine Elliot, as told by Marilyn L. Garcia

My favorite thing is to go where I've never been.
—Diane Arbus

The telephone rang and a stranger at the other end of the line asked to speak to my husband, who was not home. Suspecting she was trying to sell him something, I was very rude, but she persisted, "I am desperately looking for a photographer to go to India next week. The tourism bureau in the State of Gujarat in northwestern India is sponsoring a promotional trip and the other guy we had lined up just backed out. I was hoping to speak with him."

India—I had always wanted to go there. In an instant, I replied, "Well, I can speak for him and he will be able to go, and I'm his wife and I want to go too!"

The woman readily agreed. She knew what we did not: bordering on southern Pakistan, the State of Gujarat was seldom visited by international tourists. Its sizeable Hindu and Muslim populations meant there was significant potential for civil unrest. All I knew was that I was going to Gujarat, the place where Mahatma Gandhi was born and began his struggle for India's independence. And we decided to add a side trip to another part of India, the backwaters of Kerala—the Venice of India—on the southwest coast. With only five days to plan and pack, we rushed to obtain visas and get or confirm we were up to date on the necessary immunizations—hepatitis A, hepatitis B, typhoid, diphtheria, tetanus, meningitis and malaria. If the required immunizations were any indication, this would be an exotic trip.

We arrived in Ahmedabad, Gujarat's main city, to discover we were the only tourists there. Ahmedabad was noisy, polluted by industrial smoke, and teeming with over five million people. It showed little evidence of its former grandeur as a walled Mughal citadel, one of the largest and finest cities in India during the fifteenth century. Thank goodness we were on a promotional trip, which meant we were treated very well, staying at the Inder Residency Hotel, near Gujarat College and the main bridge over the Sabarmati River flowing through the city.

The 9-day Navaratri Dance Festival honoring an important Hindu goddess took place while we were there. From midnight until 4 a.m. people danced furiously—in their apartment courtyards and huge venues like the soccer stadium. Young women wore *gagras*—blouses, long skirts and *sari*-like sashes—of vibrant red, orange and green, and older women wore shiny *saris* embellished with gold embroidery. All wore gold jewelry and glass bangles that jangled when they danced. People danced in circles around effigies of Hindu demigods, ending each evening with dances around maypole-like posts, singing a religious song known as an *arti*. Candles made of *ghee*, Indian butter, lit their faces.

One night I became so caught up in the festivities I donned a *sari* and hopped onto the stage to dance, and my performance was shown on television. We certainly were providing the tourism bureau with plenty of material! They treated me as if I were Princess Diana—people were asking me to autograph their paper money.

Then we went to Kerala where I hoped for a luxurious three-day stay on a houseboat, replete with servants and a captain piloting us down the lush backwater canals of Kerala. It would be an understatement to say the houseboat we'd reserved was not what I had expected. The boat was small, converted from a *kettuvallam*, a traditional rice barge, propelled by human muscle and a sporadic motor. Worst of all, the boat had no towels or bed linens— we were to sleep on mats on top of plank boards, protected by mosquito nets. The crew consisted of a pilot and two cooks, and we were the only passengers. Crew members may have claimed they spoke English, but the only English words I ever heard them utter were "walk?" and "want beer?".

The backwaters were silent and peaceful. We wound through a labyrinth of lagoons, coconut palm-fringed lakes, rivers and narrow shady canals. We stopped at small settlements with tiny stores selling only basic supplies, such as seasonings, butter and beer. Although the villagers had barely claimed narrow strips of land for their settlements, they managed to keep cows, pigs and other animals there. One day a water buffalo wandered up next to me to drink from the canal and relieve himself.

We ate fish the crew caught from the canals. The cooks made the sauces with canal water, and washed the dishes with it as well. I was glad we'd had our immunizations before we left the United States, but somehow I didn't think the immunizations would protect us from the microbes and critters in those canals. I hoped the cooks were boiling the water, and the chilis, ginger and tumeric, believed to have curative powers, would protect us. Otherwise, I'd have to rely on the 330 million Hindu deities occupying this remarkable land.

But not only did I not get sick, I never even had an upset stomach. I must have good karma. Being a diabetic has never stopped me from doing anything and, in fact, I do things most people would not do, not because I am a diabetic, but because of who I am.

SIX

WALKING THROUGH TUSCANY

by Sherry Neil-Urban, as told by Marilyn L. Garcia

We say "How beautiful!" about most places. In Pisa we say nothing; it is enough to breathe.
—Elizabeth Barrett Browning

Travel is regulated exercise for me. I would be healthier if I were permanently on vacation. This lesson was brought home when I joined 15 women on a walking tour of Tuscany. I use an insulin pump, so I took plenty of catheter needles, batteries, backup insulin and syringes, and the contact information for the pump manufacturer. I adjusted to European time merely by changing my pump's clock for the basal rate to the local time, and this worked out fine for me. Upon the advice of our guides from England, I brought *trainers*—sneakers in American English—and hiking boots.

Tuscany is picture postcard countryside—rolling wooded hills, vineyards, olive groves, cypress trees, medieval and Renaissance towns, and ruins of the Etruscans, the people who occupied the area from the 8th to the 1st century BC. Our plan would be four days of walking from one town to another, with two days off in San Gimignano and Siena.

We gathered in Pisa: Linda, my friend Toni, Lois, Nancy, another Toni, Ann, Bev, Suzanne, Debbie, Karen and Kelly, all members of a walking club who had saved for five years to go on the trip, Eileen from Los Angeles, Yvonne and Lissa from Kansas City, Judy from Denver, and me. As my friend Toni said, "We're a bunch of strong-minded, fun-loving women." The fun began when our guides, Jackie and Isabel, welcomed us with Chianti and cookies. Then we were off in vans to Volterra for the first night.

Volterra seemed powerful and forbidding as we approached—a fortress on a rocky, crumbling plateau, protected by medieval walls and cylindrical projections, like castle towers. Jackie assured us that despite this grim facade Volterra began as a thriving Etruscan city. As with all the towns we would visit, Volterra did not allow motor vehicles inside its walls, so we parked near a city gate and walked to Hotel Villa Nencini near Piazza dei Priori, the main square surrounded by austere medieval mansions.

We ate a traditional Tuscan dinner of regional fish, potato/vegetable soup, fresh warm bread, and plenty of Chianti. It was here that we began to learn about each other: who was married and who was single, who had children, who had traveled frequently and who had never been out of the country before. This first dinner marked the beginning of our friendship. The following day would be our first walk—15 miles to San Gimignano.

The July heat pressed upon us, so we donned sturdy shoes, khaki shorts, sleeveless t-shirts, hats and sunglasses for the trek. We were ready for serious walking! I had never walked for five hours straight, the morning regimen, so I ate lots of cereal, bread and juice for breakfast. Taking a wild guess, I decided to stay with my basal rate on the insulin pump, and bolus one unit of rapid-acting insulin instead of my normal eight, and wondered if I would be high or low later that day.

We began by descending an ancient Etruscan path past a Roman amphitheater with marble columns into a valley of golden grass, through open country on gravel paths. We passed Etruscan tombs and eroded Etruscan walls, and spent the day sharing stories about our families and our lives. I even told everyone about my insulin pump; I didn't know then that the group's knowing about my diabetes would help me later in the trip.

We stopped for lunch along the road, for Isabel's fabulous feast—four salads, three fresh regional breads, three regional cheeses, three cured meats, three fruit tarts, three Italian wines and all the water we could drink. Each day's lunch would be equally bountiful. I tested my blood sugar and it was only 50, so I decided to take 1 1/2 units of rapid-acting insulin instead of my typical eight and test my blood sugar often. We sat on the grass under a tree to eat, welcoming the rest and the shade. I felt like a queen in a culinary extravaganza; enjoying my new friends was the best part.

In the afternoon things became more grueling when we entered rough pastures and thick oak woodland as the sun beat down. Far ahead the land rose to a ridge. I hoped San Gimignano would be on the other side, but when we reached the top, only more pastures and woodland spread out below, with another ridge on the horizon. We descended to open land, then a quiet wood with fallen trees, ivy, mushrooms and other fungi. I wondered if we would eat any of these delicacies for dinner.

My blood sugar continued to be low—47 at one point—so I ate Isabel's candies and drank plenty of water as the afternoon wore on.

Eventually we reached the second ridge. Rows of grapevines and a patchwork of agricultural color covered the valley ahead of us, and in the distance was San Gimignano. The remainder of the walk to the town leveled into less treacherous terrain through vineyards, sunflower fields and cypress trees. San Gimignano's 14 rectangular towers clustered ahead of us, like miniature skyscrapers glowing in the afternoon sun. The towers were symbols of power and wealth to the families who once lived there.

We passed through three rings of walls, entered through a 700-year-old gate, and walked down narrow streets to Hotel La Cisterna. The hotel sat on a triangular brick square with a 13th century well in its center. Great medieval houses framed the square. I was starting to feel like Helena Bonham Carter, the actress who played the heroine in the movie, *A Room With A View*.

When I settled in my room and tested my blood sugar, it was low again. I decided to lose some weight in the days ahead, which I could do while enjoying Isabel's feasts and full dinners, by lowering my basal insulin rate by 10%, rather than eating even more. Exercise was great—especially when I did it walking through Tuscany with 15 entertaining women.

That evening we celebrated surviving the 15-mile hike with a meal that included ravioli filled with cheese and thistle, a thorny bush that grows wild in Tuscany and, we learned on our walks, hurts when you touch it. We nursed sore muscles and blistered feet with Chianti and Vernaccia, the local white wine for which the town is famous. We were amazed that we had managed to stay together on that first grueling hike—from the gazelles among us who were in top physical shape and reached each milestone first, to those of us who found making it to the top of the first hill a major triumph.

The following day we explored San Gimignano. We visited the Collegiata, a church with fresco wall paintings depicting scenes from the Old and New Testaments, and a fresco of the Annunciation with the now familiar countryside peeking through a window in the background. We explored the town hall where Dante once walked and delighted in its "profane" frescoes, such as lovers bathing together, on the second floor. Then we toured the church of San Agostino where we saw a fresco of Jesus and the Virgin Mary on their knees begging God not to let angels shoot poisoned arrows at the town. I suspected the previous residents of San Gimignano had experienced such events first hand, and now understood the walls and gates.

The next morning we set off on a 12-mile walk through woods and farmland along the Via Francigena, a 10th century pilgrim route. I lowered my pump's basel rate by an additional 20% to avoid the low blood sugar situations I'd experienced, and that day my sugar levels were better. As we walked along rocky Via Francigena I could see being a pilgrim was not easy—thank goodness Jackie led us onto paved roads for part of the trip. We passed tile-roofed farmhouses and abandoned farm equipment, and took pictures of each other on haystacks and next to grapes in vineyards.

At afternoon's end we arrived at Colle val d'Elsa, laid out in a lower level, Colle Basso, and an upper level, Colle Alta, perched on a ridge overlooking the countryside. The Hotel Arnolfo where we stayed was in Colle Alta, along Via Campana, the main drag. We bought crystal and glassware for which the town is renowned; on this trip shopping was as essential as walking and wine.

The next morning we set off through fields planted with corn, grapevines, wheat and barley, across low hills to the hilltop village of Monteriggioni, encircled by seven 13th century watchtowers. Monteriggioni remains the fortified bastion it was when it served as a defensive site against the Florentines. We were having a wonderful time in the Tuscan sun, but the towers reminded us that centuries before the inhabitants of each of these towns spent a lot of time fighting each other—or praying that they would survive the next attack. After lunch under canvas umbrellas in quiet Monteriggioni we returned to Colle val d'Esta in the vans.

Our last walk was a 15-mile march to Siena, through oak and chestnut forests and limestone hills—the Montagnola—and over Monte Maggio, a mountain peak 650 meters high. It was worth the climb; as we emerged from the mountain's woods, Siena lay ahead, its bell tower beckoning us.

When we arrived, the energetic members of our group headed for the marketplace near the 16th century fortress. Siena, like the other towns we had visited, was a mix of weathered buildings on narrow streets inhabited by vibrant people. Flower pots graced many windows, lines of laundry extended above, and television satellite dishes clung to building walls. The Italian women looked chic in skirts, heeled shoes and linen blouses—I felt fashion-impaired. We gathered for a dinner of classic Sienese food, including *Panforte*, "strong bread," a rich cake of almonds, honey and candied fruit, first created for the crusaders. Even the food didn't permit us to get away from medieval religion in Tuscany.

The next day we toured Siena, one of the greatest cities in Europe during the Middle Ages. We began at its historic center, a paved brick square that in 1347—and today still—was divided by stone strips into nine segments to identify the jurisdictions of governing council members. We began at the Palazzo Publico, built around 1300. Coming from California, I was amazed that so much of what we were inhabiting was built hundreds of years before Columbus sailed to North America. The Palazzo Publico's stone gothic arches dominated the first floor, a few stories of brick rose above them, and those were topped by the Torre del Mangia with 400 steps, which we climbed. A fresco depicting good and bad government adorned the Palazzo: the good represented by a figure wearing Siena's colors, black and white, and with merchants, dancing girls and working people; the bad represented by soldiers ravaging the land.

Then we saw the cathedral, a fantastic—some in our group thought, outrageous—gothic gingerbread house, embellished with marble saints, Venetian mosaics and a black and a white marble bell tower. Inside, more than fifty dramatic scenes decorated the pavement, and dozens of granite and marble columns rose to the vault. I thought I was in Venice without the water and in Rome's Sistine Chapel at the same time.

That final afternoon I had the only serious diabetic problem of the trip. I left the hotel to get money from the bank and became disoriented. I thought, "You must get back to the square—try to remember where you are." But the more I walked, the more confused I became. Everything started to look the same. I found out later that I had passed our hotel three times and missed it. To make matters worse, I did not have any food with me. I walked for a long time, and finally encountered the group waiting for me to go to lunch.

As I came up to them, my friend Toni announced, "Sherry, you don't look good." I was sweating profusely and my blood sugar was 27! Knowing that I was a diabetic, the women eagerly offered me their candy and snacks, and waited for me to rest for 15 minutes before going to lunch.

All the exercise had caught up to me, and the drop in my blood sugar had been subtle. I didn't know how bad I'd felt until I felt good again. This incident convinced me that a lot of exercise can lower blood sugar well into the next day—and even change your metabolism.

Our last dinner together was warm and wonderful. We had enjoyed each other as we walked and visited and shared our lives during that week. We all looked a little Italian as we gathered in the restaurant in sleeveless dresses and jewelry, our effort to make our last night together special. By then I knew not only these women but their spouses, children and boyfriends as well, and knew I would see all of them again. We toasted our friendship and our accomplishments in the Tuscany hills.

SEVEN

THE TRAIN TRIP

by Marilyn L. Garcia

A good scare is worth more to man than good advice.
—Edgar Watson Howe

We arrived by cab at Zoo Station train station in Berlin two hours before our train would leave for the 5-hour trip south to Prague. Arnoldo, my husband, and our son, Marco, had visited Prague the summer before and raved about its gothic beauty. They planned to take me and our daughter, Briana, to their favorite restaurant there—a rustic establishment in the Old Town where, Arnoldo insisted, he had eaten the best chili beans ever. We intended to take a leisurely train ride to Prague, then enjoy the legendary chili beans. Little did we know our ride would turn into a long, torturous journey, and our chili bean dinner would be deferred to another day.

This would be the third stint in a month-long journey begun at a hilltop villa on the French Riviera, followed by several days in Berlin. Then we were on our way to Prague before going by train to Vienna. We had lots of luggage—nine pieces for the four of us, bags of cement so heavy we could barely lift them.

We surveyed the station. Our challenge was moving the luggage to the train tracks—if we could find them. To our right, escalators extended upward into an area full of signs we could not read; straight ahead, a block of elevators stood in the middle of the station. Arnoldo impulsively started off to the elevators with two of the heaviest bags. But Briana and I thought it wiser to first find the tracks without such a burden, then return to report on the best route and avoid lugging our bags one extra inch. When Arnoldo realized what he had undertaken—and that he would have to do most of the work—he dispatched us. First we went up the elevators to a vast covered area of tracks, walking their length, looking for any sign to indicate where our train would arrive.

Up and down we went, but the number of our train was not there.

Frustrated, we returned to the lower level and tried a different route, up the escalators, across and around the new building, to tracks going out of the station in the other direction. Finally we spotted an overhead sign with our train number. Briana dashed over to the elevator. "It's broken!" she announced dejectedly as she looked at a paper sign taped to the door.

We returned to the lower level and reported the bad news: we would have to negotiate the bags up the escalator's moving stairs. Each of us selected a piece, wrestling it onto the moving surface of a step, balancing squarely on the step below, trying not to knock down the other people who were also balancing their bags on the moving stairs. After two trips each, we were finally on the upper level, populated with all sorts of humanity and their belongings. Moving the bags had been so exhausting, I tested my blood sugar; it was low, so I treated myself to a few Lifesaver candies.

The train arrived, we found the car with our reserved seats, and somehow lifted the bags onto the train car. Finding space for the luggage was a formidable task. Arnoldo stuffed a couple of bags in the dead space near the entrance door, lifted a few onto the overhead racks, charmed a nearby couple into allowing two pieces in their foot space, and arranged the remainder around our seats.

Our car was populated with a variety of people: a couple of men, one in his late fifties with the poise of a well-heeled businessman and the other, much younger with the scruffiness of a man just starting out; a woman in her late sixties who carried herself as an intrepid traveler; and a family of five from Venezuela—a dependable father, his outgoing wife, a couple of pretty daughters in their twenties, and a teenaged son who did not want to be responsible for much.

Once the train began to move, I walked to the dining car and asked the man behind the counter if he could store my long-acting Lantus insulin in the refrigerator. He cheerfully obliged. My doctor had insisted I chill the Lantus at all times and I had compulsively complied, knowing it was essential to my very survival. I kept the rapid-acting Humalog insulin with me and settled in for what I thought would be a peaceful journey to Prague.

The train moved out of the city through the industrial blocks that seem to fill the vistas of a train journey, into country of golden grass, thick trees and housing clusters as the train lulled us into a contemplative state. About an hour into the journey, the train came to an abrupt halt. At first we thought nothing of it, but people began to whisper that something was terribly wrong. The lady from Venezuela, whom Arnoldo had befriended in

Spanish conversation, knew the most. According to her, the train had run over someone and we would be delayed while the authorities conducted an investigation.

"I remember feeling a thump right before we stopped!" Arnoldo exclaimed.   So we waited, anxious, curious and frustrated. People made their way down to the dining car. Out the window we saw men in yellow jackets and thick gloves tromping along the side of the train, their heads down. Occasionally a tidbit of information passed through the car. One report said the train's conductor had been so traumatized by hitting the body he had been relieved of his duties. Another report questioned whether the death was a murder or a suicide, the body being on the tracks at the time of impact. Men in black uniforms marched down the aisle of our car; outside men in white coats marked by red cross patches on their sleeves made their way along the tracks.

Arnoldo reported they were giving food away. We had brought food with us, so I did not need to take them up on their offer, but after a couple of hours, I walked to the dining car to see what was going on. Upon seeing a line of people extending well past the door, I gave up and returned to my seat. "I'm not *that* hungry, even if it is free," I decided.

We saw men in suits stride by outside—could they be the inspectors, the Columbos of Germany? We saw the men in yellow jackets again, this time with heavy bags, trudge through the tall grass. We wondered if the bags could hold the body, in pieces. More men in black uniforms marched through the car. The lady from Venezuela went to the front of the train to find out more information, but she returned shaking her head in disappointment. Even more bored and hungry, I again went to the dining car, but the guy behind the counter told me all the food and drinks had been taken.

Three and a half hours later—more than six hours since arriving at the Zoo Station—the train began to move, and everyone cheered. I was relieved that we were on our way and hoped the problems were behind us. The countryside vistas resumed. Suddenly two men in German police uniforms approached me. One mumbled something I could not understand and thrust the Lantus insulin into my hands. I protested but he refused to listen, turned, and stomped down the aisle. According to my doctor, the Lantus needed to be refrigerated, and we had four hours to go before we would reach Prague. "Arnoldo, this has got to be cold! They've put a new crew on and they don't want the responsibility of keeping it in the fridge! What are we going to do?" We were both consumed with concern but had no answers. I felt helpless as the train continued on its journey.

We then arrived at the Dresden station. I associate Dresden, Germany with the horrible bombing during World War II. The train station seemed from that era, a dilapidated shell. We waited in the station for a suspiciously longer time than it should have taken to permit passengers to disembark. The train moved forward, then back, forward, then back.

But I remained obsessed with the Lantus. "Arnold, we need to get this chilled! There has to be some ice, even in this train station. This will be the last opportunity to chill this stuff! We have to get off!" He refused to get off, unsure what the train station might have and of what might happen to us if we disembarked. I was disappointed at his decision, but remained on the train, frustrated we could not solve the problem but unwilling to venture into the station by myself.

We saw the dining car on the adjacent track as we pulled out of the station. Now we knew what had happened. They had uncoupled the dining car from the train—it had no food left, it was useless, dead weight—and the train's conductors were intent on making up as much time as possible. We realized it wasn't that the German guards did not want any responsibility when they returned the Lantus to me. They had known the dining car would be removed from the train, and in all of the confusion, they had remembered to return my medicine. Attempting to find a solution, Arnoldo put the Lantus on the windowsill where small bursts of cool air occasionally emerged from a vent. We were skeptical his solution would work.

As we approached the border with the Czech Republic, three Czech guards marched down the aisle, demanding to see everyone's identification. They were no-nonsense: everyone's papers would be subject to a thorough inspection. But I continued to be alarmed about the Lantus and Arnoldo obligingly walked to the end of the car where guards had congregated. A woman with a baby and her husband with only Italian papers and no visa to enter the Czech Republic were arguing with the guards as Arnoldo tried to approach them to plead for ice. But they were too busy evicting the man from the train. "These Czechs show no mercy," she screamed as he was escorted off, leaving his wife and child behind. "They don't deserve to become members of the European Union!" Sensing that the guards would not help, Arnoldo returned to his seat.

We arrived at the Prague station at 7:40 p.m., almost four hours late. Our driver was waiting for us despite the late hour. He enlisted two wiry, tanned men with tattoos and bad teeth who did pick up jobs carrying luggage at the station. Between them, they carried all our bags to the van and we were off to the hotel. "Drive faster to the hotel," I demanded, still frantic, but then, realizing this was the very last thing I could do, I settled back and asked the driver: "Didn't the Rolling Stones perform a concert here a few weeks ago?"

When we arrived at our hotel, I stored the Lantus in the room's minibar refrigerator. That evening I took it, hoping it had not deteriorated. The next day my blood sugar levels were normal. The Lantus had been preserved.

We saw many of our fellow train passengers later in our trip. I doubt any of us would have remembered anyone else if it had not been for the train disaster. We saw the Venezuelan family during a tour of Prague's Hapsburg castle; we saw the two men at the Prague train station when we took the train to Vienna; and another man approached us at St. Stephan's Cathedral in Vienna to ask us if we had been on that fateful ride.

The epilogue of this misadventure is that some diabetic friends later told me they are not as rigorous as I have been in chilling their Lantus insulin and have been fine, but my doctor still insists that I keep it cold.

EIGHT

CONNECTING FLIGHTS

by Marilyn L. Garcia

Experience is a good teacher, but she sends in terrific bills.—Mina Antrim

In retrospect it was a dumb thing to do. When I packed for the family trip to Spain I kept a full set of my medical supplies in my purse with me, and packed the backup insulin, protected in a cold pack, and the extra blood sugar test kit in the checked luggage, under the twisted logic that it was better to divide up my supplies just in case something happened. Maybe it was a reaction to having lost my insulin during our first trip to Paris, when all my supplies were in our carry-on bags.

The itinerary for Arnoldo, Briana, Marco and me set out a 5-hour American Airlines flight from LAX international airport in Los Angeles to JFK international airport serving New York City, with a transfer to an Iberia flight leaving one hour later for arrival in Madrid the next morning. We landed at JFK half an hour behind schedule—not bad for JFK—to discover the Iberia gates were in another terminal. We tore through the terminal, stopping at a fork in the hall to get our bearings, running on. Just when it looked hopeless, a man who looked like the actor Morgan Freeman drove up in an elongated golf cart. "You folks look like you need a lift," he offered.

"We're late for an Iberia flight and it's in another terminal!" we exclaimed in unison, and jumped on.

"Don't worry, I'll have you there in no time!" We sped through the terminal, down a construction ramp, into a plywood tunnel through a construction zone, to a new terminal, and through its halls to the gate for the flight to Madrid. We'd made it. We hustled onto the plane.

The next morning, we arrived at the Madrid airport, sweaty, dirty and sleep-deprived, and went to the baggage claim area, but our luggage never appeared on the conveyer belt. Our luck had run out. We explained our predicament to the Iberia attendants, and they gave us each a canvas bag containing soap, a plastic toothbrush, toothpaste and a gray t-shirt, assuring us our bags would be delivered to the hotel when the next Iberia flight from JFK arrived.

As they say about the weather in Madrid: nine months of *invierno* and three months of *infierno*. (Nine months of winter and three months of sweltering hell.) It was August and the temperature was 42 degrees centigrade—over 112 degrees Fahrenheit. I imagined our baggage sitting for hours on an airport platform, the cold pack expired and the backup insulin overheated. We spent the day loitering around the hotel, trying to adjust to the new time, feeling very sorry for ourselves in dirty underwear and gray t-shirts.

"You have to see the swimming pool on the roof!" Marco reported.

"Marco," Briana pressed, "you haven't told the whole story."

"Uh, OK," he stammered. "A lot of the people up there are topless, just like on the Riviera and in Rhodes."

Our only other accomplishment that day was discovering that a German youth symphony also were guests—the kids with the tubas were hard to miss in the elevators.

The baggage arrived at the hotel that evening and the coldpack was warm. Not knowing how overheated the insulin had become, I discarded it. That would be the last time I put any supplies in checked baggage!

NINE

SPANISH DINNER TIME

by Marilyn L. Garcia

*3 o'clock is always too late or too early for anything
you want to do.*—Jean Paul Sartre

I n Madrid, Isabelle and Joan—Catalán for
John—introduced us to Spanish dinner time,
which rarely starts before 9:30 p.m., and is more
likely to begin at 10 p.m. Isabelle, an endocrinologist, observed that Spanish dinner time meant diabetics did not suffer from low blood sugar during

the night, but an afternoon *merienda* (type of snack) was a must.

"You have to try this *morcilla*—then I'll tell you what it is," Isabelle insisted as appetizers arrived at Casa Valencia which served the best *paella* in Madrid. Glancing at the dry, black clumps of *morcilla* before me, then at my wine glass to make sure it was full, I dashed some down, followed with a gulp of wine.   Isabelle and Joan were such gracious hosts that I was willing to do things I might ordinarily refuse to do.

"*Morcilla* is sausage made only from blood!" she announced. Then the *paellas* arrived in metal pans, adorned with tasteless seafood, meats and vegetables, their flavors having been absorbed by the glorious rice.

Another night we toured the *tapas* bars of Plaza Santa Ana, a square teaming with Spaniards sufficiently energetic to enjoy themselves well into the next morning. Nearby stands the house where Cervantes lived. Isabelle and Joan navigated the narrow side streets, stopping at the *tapas* bars for their specialties—Cerveceria Alemana, a Hemingway haunt, for serrano ham and drinks, La Casa del Abuelo for grilled shrimp and red wine, Las Bravas for fried potatoes with spicy tomato sauce and grilled baby octopus, and another, my favorite, for grilled asparagus. Unknown to us then, these late dinners in Madrid would not be the latest dinner we would consume during our trip.

We were touring Spain in a rented van, arriving at the end of each day in a new town, usually without hotel reservations. Arnoldo planned to drive the stint from Algeciras, near Gibralter, around the Mediterranean coast to Barcelona—800 miles—in one day. We left Algeciras on multi-laned freeways through land that looked like Southern California— the word "California" being from a miscommunication among the Spanish conqueror *Cortéz's* soldiers, who reported that the land was *caliente como un horno* (hot like an oven), or its Latin equivalent, *calida fornax*. The soldiers couldn't pronounce the Latin version and changed the words to California.

About noon we arrived in Granada, where the Moors built their Alhambra summer palace during the 14th and 15th centuries in the city's hills. We had not planned in advance to tour the Alhambra. As we made our way up the hill, boys waved people to a special parking area, guiding tourists' cars into parking places and collecting their money. We decided to park at the top of the hill in a paved lot adjacent to the Alhambra's main entrance. But we discovered tickets were sold out until late afternoon, so we returned to our van and drove down the hill. At the special parking area, parking tickets fluttered from every car's windshield, and the boys were gone. Only then did we notice that the No Parking signs had been covered with brown paper.

Just outside Granada we decided to stop for a late lunch. The freeway exit with the "Food and Gasoline" sign was temporarily closed, so we took the next one, marked "Detour," intending to get back on the freeway in the other direction to the gas station. Instead we impulsively proceeded along a road that wound through an area scattered with houses, some partially built. The road was not leading us to any commercial areas, but we continued even as it narrowed into the hills. Eventually we decided to turn around into a dirt driveway that led down a hill to a house. But when Arnoldo put the gears in reverse, the van's front wheels only spun in the loose dirt.

We emerged from the van into sweltering heat and tried to stabilize the wheels with discarded boards, but the wheels continued to spin, digging the van deeper and deeper into a hole, angling it even more downward. It was very hot, and we were very, very stuck. Although I knew we would get out of this jam, I had no idea how long it would take or how it would happen. At least my insulin would be chilled for the remainder of the day in the coolpack and we had food in the van; if we were stuck for a longer time, we had big problems!

We had not seen a single person since exiting the freeway. The driveway descended through a barren area, an olive grove on one side, and the remnants of a garden nearby. The house below was unoccupied and a narrow stream of water flowed down the hill toward the house. A car finally zoomed by and we waved frantically, but it did not stop. We waited under the olive tree, then in the van, wondering what would happen. While the children played in a hut in the middle of the olive grove, Arnoldo went up to the road to look for a good Samaritan who might offer some help. Finally, an old Otis forklift heavy with a load of bricks rounded the bend, driven by a man well past his prime. He must have been working at one of the local construction sites. Arnoldo waived him down.

"*Disculpe, señor*" (excuse me, sir), Arnoldo shouted over the sound of the engine; the man stopped and turned it off. "*Tuvimos un acidente*" (we had an accident), he explained, and continued, "Our van is stuck and we cannot drive it out of the embankment. We need help towing it out."

The old man listened intently. Evidently satisfied with the explanation, he dismounted the forklift to assess the situation. Solving the problem would require attaching a cable to the van's rear axle and gradually pulling it up the nearly 30 feet of sloping hill to the paved road. The old man picked up a wire used for fencing grazing areas that was lying in the dirt. The man's even thinking this wire could be used for such a heavy job told us he would not bring any strategic judgment to the task. Arnoldo and the man nevertheless attached the wire to the axle and the forklift and attempted a tow, but the wire snapped without moving the van. The man agreed to go for a chain; we watched as he slowly drove off, not knowing if he would return.

More than an hour passed, and we began to doubt that he would come back. Some time later he did, announcing, *"Perdone la demora, estoy trabajando en la construccion de una casa y tenia que entregar los ladrillos en el pueblo. Por eso es que me tarde tanto."* (Excuse my tardiness, but I am part of a construction crew building a house and I had to deliver the load of bricks to the building site before I could return to help you.) We appreciated the help all the more. The old man then pulled out a rope that obviously would not be strong enough for the job. *Ay, caramba!!* we all thought to ourselves. After more cajoling from Arnoldo, he finally pulled out a decently sturdy chain. Sliding himself under the van, Arnoldo tied the chain to the van's axle and then to the forklift.

But this was not the end of it. The dirt driveway curved over a ledge that sloped down the hill. As the forklift began to pull the van up the driveway, the van did not turn along the driveway's curve, its wheels coming within an inch of the crumbly edge. "Stop! Stop!" we screamed, loud enough to penetrate the engine noise and cause the driver to stop. It was a near miracle the van did not go over the edge and tumble down the hill. Taking command,

Arnoldo gave the driver specific instructions to avoid another disaster, and a few minutes later the forklift pulled the van to the top of the driveway.

Arnoldo dove under the van again and unhooked the cable, careful to fold it properly, and handed it to the driver. *"Muchisimas gracias señor. Espero no le haigamos quitado mucho tiempo."* (Thank you very much, sir. I hope we have not taken up too much of your time.) Extending his hand, Arnoldo continued to speak. "We owe you a great deal *señor*. "My family and I would be most grateful if you would accept a little something for your efforts."

The man raised his hand indicating thanks were sufficient, but Arnoldo persisted and extended his hand again to deliver our monetary token of appreciation. The driver reluctantly accepted and asked only that we proceed with caution on the rest of our trip. And at 4 o'clock in the afternoon, we were on our way to Barcelona—only 500 miles to go.

The remainder of the drive was long, frantic and grueling. German cars passed us even as we hit speeds near 90 miles an hour. The coast evolved into clusters of massive high rise luxury apartment buildings. As we approached Valencia, the hills became an undulating emerald carpet dotted with infinite oranges. Diabetics are advised to drink orange juice when they have low blood sugar; now I knew where the entire world's supply came from!

Our odyssey became even more difficult after

dark. Arnoldo was so exhausted he occasionally dozed off, nearly veering off the freeway, but he refused to stop for the night. Near midnight, we approached the lights of Barcelona, without hotel reservations, filthy from our efforts in the Granada hills. We drove through an industrial area to a grand boulevard, the Diagonal, one of Barcelona's main drags. Spotting a violet neon sign atop a highrise— IN ERCONTINENTAL—we drove to the entrance.

The Intercontinental hotel was more expensive than our usual quarters, but at that point we would have paid any price for shelter and showers. "Arnold, you are filthy," I said. "I bet they won't give us rooms." Arnoldo put on a jacket to hide his disheveled state and, speaking Spanish, asked the bellhop at the curb if the hotel had rooms available, arming himself with this information just in case he was not welcomed at the front desk.

"*Si, señor,*" the bellhop replied, and Arnoldo went inside. We did get rooms, and ordered food from room service. To this day all of us remember what we ordered—I ordered eggs and asparagus— because it was the best meal we ate in Spain!

TEN

TURBULENCE

by Marilyn L. Garcia

(Airplanes) may kill you, but they ain't likely to hurt you.—Satchell Paige

We had survived the trip to Spain—the delayed baggage and the cliffhanger in the Granada hills—and were safely, so far, packed in economy class on a full jumbo jet home. I suspected the journey would be more interesting than the usual plane flight, given the three characters seated in front of us: a striking Black woman and her two children, a girl about seven, wearing bright pink pants, whose name I never learned, and a boy about three, named Francois. We knew his name because his mother constantly told him to stop squirming or to sit down.

At least Francois and his sister broke the tedium. Once we were airborne and the fasten seat belt sign was turned off, the girl spent most of her time dancing up and down the aisles in fluid acrobatic moves to an internal rhythm only she could compose. As I watched her, I wished I could dance like that but resigned myself to enjoying the show. Francois was the real terror, a center of turbulence unto himself. He squirmed. "Francois, be still," his mother ordered. He climbed under the seat. "Francois, get out from under there." He kicked the seat in front of him. "Francois, stop that!" Francois and his sister were so creatively energetic I didn't mind the commotion, but I wasn't the passenger whose seat he kicked.

Several hours into the flight the attendants began preparations for a meal, and I headed back to the restroom to take my insulin. Sometimes people asked me if I would take a shot in front of people, say, at a restaurant, instead of going to the restroom. I suspected they had witnessed diabetics doing such things. I hate shots, except for one's I held myself, so I usually excused myself. But the frequency of the question has encouraged me to be less conservative lately. On my last plane flight, I discreetly, I thought, took a shot in my airplane seat. But a few minutes later the woman next to me launched into a long confession about how she had become a diabetic while she was pregnant and couldn't stand the needles, which goes to show that people notice everything, know more than you think they do, and are usually cool about it.

As I walked down the aisle, the plane began to shake as processed air hissed through the cabin. By the time I'd reached the back, the pilot announced that people should return to their seats and fasten their seat belts. But I figured I'd gone this far, so I ignored his order and entered the bathroom instead. I filled a syringe with insulin, bracing myself with my feet against the walls. When things settled down I began the shot. But just then, the plane made a huge seismic shift—a 9 on the Richter scale in earthquake terms. I pulled the syringe away from me, barely avoiding breaking the needle in me, as I bumped against the wall and nearly fell down, dropping the full syringe on the floor in the process.

That had never happened before. Shaken, and not knowing when the next bout of turbulence would occur, I cleaned up the mess and decided to take the shot when things settled down.

Many hours later we approached JFK international airport to land. The pilot battled the plane to the ground and we hit so hard that one of the overhead bins exploded open. It was the bin directly above Francois.

CHECKPOINT CHARLIE

by Mike Acosta, as told by Marilyn L. Garcia

A thick skin is a gift from God.
—Konrad Adenauer

I knew there was going to be trouble when I saw the *fraulein* guards rough up the lady ahead of me in the security line at Tegel airport in Berlin. Despite the talk of the New Berlin, I was beginning to suspect a Teutonic past dies hard.

I was returning from a business trip to Berlin where the company I work for had product distributors. Since becoming a type-1 diabetic a few years before, the trips had added the complications of dealing with insulin and eating schedules, but I'd done well, always keeping my medication and prescriptions with me. But this post-9/11 world created a different atmosphere when I traveled, especially in Germany. Mostly it was the machine guns that the airport guards carried. I had seen such things in airports in Mexico, and in Rome outside the banks, but in the Berlin airport when I was on business, it was unnerving.

Then it was my turn to put my backpack on the conveyer belt for screening, but a plastic barrier blocked items bigger than a large purse, including my backpack. That's when one of the *Brunhildas* picked it up and began to inspect its contents. She found the open package of syringes and she changed her attitude for the worse.

She didn't speak English, and neither did her compatriot, and I didn't speak German. Waiving the prescription form and pointing to the insulin bottle, I tried to explain I needed the medicine. They would have none of it. Through the grunts and the gestures, they made it clear the only thing I could carry on board was a paperback book. The backpack with my medications inside would have to be checked into the cargo hold. I was shocked—how could medicine and syringes with tiny needles, accompanied by official prescriptions, be terrorists' tools? The open package of syringes must have tipped the scales.

My voice became urgent and shrill as I protested and my mind raced... "I don't like being without my medication for over 12 hours. What if the backpack gets lost? I'm not sure I have another bottle at home and I will arrive on a Sunday when I can't buy more. These guards don't know they're being shortsighted in carrying out orders. If I get sick on the flight they may have to land the plane—I'd heard about that from a friend, who didn't feel well on his flight from Paris to Los Angeles, and they had to land the plane in Ireland! What would they think about that!?!"

As I argued, I could see I was only escalating things; the guards were about to escort me over to the guys with the machine guns and have me thrown off the flight. Despite being ten generations removed from my Iberian forbearers, I suspected the Moorish elements in that past might mean I'd end up in the jail with real terrorist suspects. That's when I gave up and let them stuff the syringes and insulin into the backpack and confiscate it for the cargo hold. All I could do was hope I would be OK and the backpack would show up when I got off the plane in San Francisco.

The 12-hour flight home seemed to take forever. I was tempted to deal with my anxiety by behaving like the typical business class passenger—belt down the free champagne, then hit the hard stuff all the way through the flight, but I didn't. Eventually the flight arrived at San Francisco international airport, and my backpack was waiting for me at the luggage carousel.

TWELVE

BICYCLING IN THE SHADOW OF THE MING

by Catherine Elliot, as told by Marilyn L. Garcia

The journey is the reward.
—Tao saying

I n 1988, my husband and I took a bicycle trip around the northwestern part of China with a group of ten other intrepid souls. China was not like it is today, with its more than 50 McDonald's in Beijing alone, and English speakers were few and far between. At least our group was escorted by Chinese guides in a couple of vans to provide basic assistance for blown out tires and thirsty riders.

One day we planned to cycle from the outskirts of Beijing to the Ming Tombs located in a valley about 30 miles away. Even then the Ming Tombs were a highlight for foreign visitors, the place where most of the Ming dynasty emperors were buried. Our goal was to ride out to the renovated tomb built in 1427 for Emperor Yongle, who was responsible for building the Forbidden City in Beijing, picnic among the ruins, and possibly ride out to the unrestored tombs lying farther up the valley.

The ride started out uneventfully enough, with our group making its way out of the city on paved roads to rolling countryside with villages and farms. But I became frustrated with the slow pace of the group and sped ahead. As I enjoyed my freedom, the fresh air, and the corn and melon fields along the way, I noticed I was all alone, the stragglers nowhere to be seen. It was still morning, so I proceeded into a village and got off my bike, among Chinese peasants in drab pajama-like garb who had never seen a Caucasian before except, maybe, on television. Because I was wearing skin-tight blue spandex and a helmet, they behaved—and reasonably so—as if I had just arrived from Mars.

The villagers cautiously approached me, talking in a nasal jabber, then began to poke me to see if I was real. Beijing was full of heavy proletarian bicycles with front baskets, but the villagers acted as if they had never seen a 10-speed bike before. I should have been grateful they didn't begin to take it apart, like the Chinese did to the airplane that mistakenly entered their airspace and was forced to land there a few years before.

At that point I was not worried. I had a Power Bar and did not need to eat anything; I did not require a meal until I took a boost of short-acting insulin. The real problem was I didn't have a map and had no idea where I was. "Ming Tombs" I announced, but the villagers just stared at me. I was becoming concerned but decided not to panic, if for no other reason than it wouldn't do any good.

Eventually I found the police station, a drab concrete bunker. I entered and repeated, "Ming Tombs, Ming Tombs," over and over, but no one understood. Now I *was* worried: what if it got dark? At some point being a diabetic without my long-acting insulin *would* be a problem. And after a full two hours in the village, I was close to panicking: I didn't want to end up in my own Ming Tomb! Finally I realized I was going to have to rescue myself by retracing my steps—wheel tracks—back where I had come from. Surely the bike group would notice I wasn't with them.

So I biked out of town and found the main road where I ran into some soldiers. Maybe someone had notified them that a space alien had entered their farmlands and they had come to investigate. The soldiers accompanied me to where the bike group and vans were waiting. I must have been quite a sight—a helmeted road warrior escorted by the vestiges of Mao's army. I had become lost because I'd failed to turn at the fork in the road. My husband was furious. With no concern about my well-being, he roared, "This is a *group tour,* you know!"

My riding ahead had been a crazy thing to do, but it had nothing to do with being a diabetic. In the short time I had been lost, my diabetes had not been a factor. I have traveled to Vietnam, Laos, Cambodia, Kenya, Peru, Chile and Argentina, without having any diabetic problems other than a few low blood sugar reactions, but I have those at home too. Now I always remember to bring a map wherever I go.

THIRTEEN

WHAT WE LEFT IN PARIS

by Marilyn L. Garcia

"Why not" is an interesting slogan for an interesting life.—Mason Cooley

I t was early March and I wasn't busy at the office when my husband commented as he read the morning paper, "United is advertising flights to Paris for $199 each way."

That was all it took for me to show up outside my daughter's English class later that day and ask:

"Do you have anything going on next week? How would you like to go to Paris?"

Briana was in her last semester of high school and had already been accepted to college, so it didn't seem like an irresponsible thing to do. She could practice her French and work on the color photo project for her photography class, and I could conduct business by telephone. One week later, we arrived in the City of Light in the cold and imminently rainy weather justifying the cheap plane tickets. But the off season offered other benefits: the places we avoided during the crowded high season because of long lines—the Louvre, the Pompidou Center—would be accessible.

This escapade would be our third mother-daughter trip to Paris. The first day would be as it always was: dropping our bags at the hotel and heading straight for *Printemps* department store, seven levels of glorious clothes, shoes and other merchandise, with a visit to its restaurant under a domed skylight of multi-colored glass that escaped destruction during World War II. It was our way of easing into the stuffy Paris museums.

The first day provided reassurances for diabetics who travel to France. Our hotel was located in the 9th *Arrondissement* (neighborhood) behind the Opera—near *Printemps!*—and I noticed that each short block had a pharmacy indicated by a green neon sign. I took this as a signal that we were in a residential neighborhood, which may have been true, but I have since learned the French medical system is structured so that the French use significantly more prescription medications than people in other first world countries. Despite any problems that may result, the plentiful green neon signs are a welcome sight for diabetics. It means medications are readily available.

Printemps had changed, too. As we wandered through the store, sales announcements came over the loudspeaker in English. While this development may have been a grave disappointment to the French, who value language purity, it demonstrates that these days it is very easy to find someone to assist you who speaks English.

So this trip to Paris was about taking color pictures of unexpected things in the gray, wet weather: the gaggle of motor scooters—red, blue, yellow and black—parked between lampposts on Boulevard Hausmann; and the two Smart cars, half the length of a typical automobile—one blue, one red—parked along a curb with their front fenders touching each other as if the two were kissing.

Sherbet-colored posters advertising i-Pods covered the walls in the subway tunnels where we discovered the most amazing fruit stands. We first smelled the fruit before rounding a tunnel corner to come upon the stand, tended by a man playing a wooden flute. Other colorful fruit and vegetable stands dotted the Marais quarter, the oldest Parisian neighborhood first laid out in the 13th century. The stands dominated the Marais's narrow streets, in stark contrast to the cold stone buildings.

We saw color along a street near the Left Bank's Museum Cluny which showcases subterranean Roman baths and artifacts from Paris's medieval era—iron tools, manuscripts, armor, ivories, sculpture and tapestries, including the famous Lady and the Unicorn. The color we noticed was on a nearby building wall: a replica of the medieval tapestries painted on the wall had been almost obliterated by graffiti.

And we found perfect yellow on the rainiest of days in the Luxembourg gardens: the color of the oil-skin raincoat on a little boy chasing pigeons, and in the beds of meticulously planted pansies along the puddled paths near the Marie de Medici Palace. These walks were great for my blood sugar control; the test results were perfect—90 to 100—virtually all of the time.

We were also determined to sample pastries at the legendary Pierre Herme. I had first heard of this place a few years before, knowing only its address: 72 Rue Bonaparte on the Left Bank. On a previous Paris trip we'd attempted to go there but found a closed shop, covered with a corrugated tin door. The sign—Pierre Herme—suggested to us a clothing boutique, not a pastry shop. We later learned that Pierre

Herme, the man, was considered the greatest pastry chef in the world, and we had arrived at his establishment on the first day it had closed for the August vacation.

On this trip we were more successful and entered a narrow shop filled with culinary works of art, the most memorable being small chocolate cakes constructed into castles, and macaroons. We selected a chocolate tart, neon green macaroons, a pink tart topped with raspberries, and chocolate-covered hazelnuts for gifts. We ate half our prizes and deposited the remainder in our room's refrigerator. The chocolate tart was the best quality; eating it didn't cause my blood sugar to rise when I took only a few units of Humalog to compensate for the treat.

Our four days in Paris passed and we ended up at Charles de Gaulle Airport to return home. The last color I remember was the poster at the airport that advertised a French mobile phone company; in the background, behind the individual with a mobile phone, lurked the skyline of Los Angeles!

Once in the air, we settled in for two long flights—de Gaulle to Dulles Airport in the Washington, D.C. area, then Dulles to LAX—home. When we were halfway over the Atlantic Ocean, something occurred to me: I had left my insulin in the refrigerator at the hotel. I could easily believe this had happened. Since all of my insulin except the open bottle of rapid-acting Humalog was refrigerated, whether on the road or at home, I usually wrote a note to remind myself not to forget it when I left, knowing how the last minute, as one is rushing to leave for a trip, invites the possibility of forgetting something, whether it is insulin or airplane tickets. But this time I had not done that, with the not-surprising result. The absurd part was that Briana had removed our Pierre Herme pastries from the refrigerator, but we didn't have the insulin.

One problem was I had taken two bottles of each kind of insulin on the trip, as recommended, which meant there was none waiting for me at home. The other problem was it was a Sunday—mid-day at the time of our departure and over the Atlantic Ocean, as our plane stayed even with the local time—but we would not arrive in Los Angeles until Sunday evening, after the pharmacies had closed.

At first I just sat there and acknowledged the situation. Then I began to think about what to do. My first thought was to imagine—wish, really—the pharmacy would still be open. Then I thought maybe we could find another pharmacy open late. But I needed a prescription for the long-acting Lantus insulin, and not all pharmacies carried it. It also meant a call to my doctor for the prescription. Should I disturb him? Maybe I should just show up at the emergency room; after all, one had to pay for mistakes every once in a while. Or maybe I could just survive for 24 hours without Lantus by taking successive shots of rapid-acting Humalog.

After mulling over which of these alternatives would be the best—it hit me: I could call the pharmacy while we were still traveling and my husband could purchase the insulin before the pharmacy closed and we arrived in Los Angeles. Was this a stroke of genius, or had it taken me longer than most people to figure out this easy solution? The answer didn't matter as long as it had come to me. And I even had the phone number of the pharmacy with me.

All we had to do upon arrival at Dulles Airport was endure the delay of disembarkation—waiting our turn to shuffle to the door of the plane, a shuttle ride to the terminal, then immigration and customs—the sea of humanity waiting for immigration processing in the post-9/11 world, sorting people into U.S. citizen and non-U.S. citizen categories. Most important for me, we couldn't use a cell phone until clearing customs. This draconian world was different from the system in place during our first mother-daughter shopping spree to Paris, when the U.S. Customs agent, with a twinkle in his eye, welcomed us back to the United States: "I see you sisters had a good time in France."

Finally we were in an area where I could use my cell phone. We stepped off to the side and I pulled out my rarely-used phone, grateful I had decided to bring it with me. Wondering whether the pharmacist had ever been called by a customer traveling from Paris, I spoke efficiently: "Hello. I am one of your customers and I am traveling from Europe right now and forgot my Lantus insulin in Europe. I won't arrive in Pasadena until after you close. Would it be possible for you to have another bottle ready within the next hour and someone will come and pick it up?" The pharmacist assured me it would be done.

FOURTEEN

THE CLIFFS OF SANTORINI

by Marilyn L. Garcia

In the world of mules there are no rules.
—Ogden Nash

Our tender boat rocked so violently in the sea I wondered whether we would reach the shore. This treachery belied the stunning vista before us: the Skala harbor of the Greek island of Santorini that provides one of the most spectacular views of an island in the world. The harbor is the remnant of the enormous crater formed when a volcano blew out the island's center about 1450 B.C. The cataclysm created a harbor ringed by jagged mountains emerging from the water, including the island's cliffs rising before us—garnished with chalk-white buildings and roads zigzagging up the side. The town of Fira iced the pinnacle.

On that day we would—we hoped anyway, at that moment in the sea—visit Santorini as part of a two-week cruise for families of ancient sites in the Mediterranean. The cruise had begun at a dock in Civitavecchia, the port city serving Rome. As we had waited on the dock to board the ship, we noticed a man carrying a cello case, accompanied by his wife and two children, causing Arnoldo to remark, "Look at that guy, taking a cello on his family vacation. He's probably going to make his children practice. Who does he think he is, Yo Yo Ma?" Several days into the cruise, we discovered he *was* Yo Yo Ma, on vacation with his family. It was Yo Yo, not his kids, who practiced the cello on that trip.

Back at the Skala harbor off Santorini, our tender finally reached land, and we were hustled onto buses for a visit to Akrotiri—the "Minoan Pompeii"—abandoned when the volcano exploded. At Akrotiri we entered a gargantuan metal shed covering the ruins of a multi-layered city of thousands. We walked along a main street and peered into rooms and balconies. Huge earthen jars stood in rows, reminders of the plentiful stores of olive oil and grain they once held. Paintings of the festive Minoan culture decorated some walls. Recently scholars discovered man's first use of plants as medicine 3,500 years ago based on a Santorini painting depicting a goddess making a drug from the saffron flower.

As the afternoon ended we returned to Fira, and were left to our own devices, with instructions to be at the Skala harbor below no later than 9:30 p.m. for tenders back to the ship. To do this, we could take the cable car, ride donkeys or walk. In the meantime, Fira's whitewashed buildings and narrow streets crowded with tourists formed a maze of stores, mostly selling jewelry. We decided to follow a couple of fellow passengers at a discreet distance, hoping they would lead us to a suitable restaurant, and ended up at an establishment with a stunning view at the edge of the cliff.

The restaurant welcomed us with dark wooden furniture, tablecloths illuminated with candles and suspiciously obliging waiters. We proceeded to order a Greek feast. We could see our ship, lit up like a Christmas tree in the center of the Skala harbor below, looking like a toy. We also had a good vantage point to watch the cable cars descending to the harbor. As we waited for the food, we witnessed the swaying cable cars. "Mom, if you don't want to leave your dinner on Santorini, we better not take those cable cars," Marco observed.

Anticipating dinner when we ordered the food, I took some Humalog, but more than an hour later our food had not been served, and no amount of fidgeting, fuming and pestering caused it to materialize. At least the waiter brought me some orange juice in the interim, and the repast eventually arrived. Later we learned that this different sense of time is customary in restaurants in Greece. It also meant a delay in returning to the ship.

We hurried along the narrow streets, deciding to walk down the zigzagged donkey path because we didn't want to take the swaying cables cars and none of us had ridden a donkey before. But I knew we had made the wrong choice after the first zig and before the first zag. The path, lined with smooth cobble stones, angled steeply downward. The route must have been the equivalent of Santorini's "rapid transit line," with stopping points where donkeys and their masters gathered. I led the march down while Arnoldo shepherded from behind to make certain the children didn't get too close to the rear end of a donkey.

Then I made a strategic decision. I was wearing loafers with leather soles that would not hold my footing. The official medical advice for diabetics is to wear comfortable shoes and socks, but these were extenuating circumstances. If I didn't take those shoes off I would surely end up on my rear—in donkey dung. I removed the shoes, figuring my bare feet would provide a better grip, and dreading the inevitable.

We continued down the path, which grew longer with each blind turn. Each turn only brought a new stretch of darkness and donkeys. The path seemed miles long—how could this be? "Nice donkey," I whispered as I passed each one, hoping to deter a kick. We could barely make out our surroundings, and the water below seemed very far away.

We rounded each bend expecting it would be the last, only to be confronted by more cobbled path. We laughed as we encouraged each other to press on through the darkness. With each step I expected to meet warm donkey droppings, but it never happened. We were on the path only ten minutes before the ship's deadline, but a few minutes later we rounded a corner and reached the end of that serpentine journey, dashing for the tender, with less than five minutes to spare.

We visited many ancient sites during the remainder of the cruise, but the activities on board brought the unique amusements. Some took place in the dining room at dinner. Cruise ships prepare elegant multi-course dinners for passengers, as part of the lure of a glamorous cruise, but the many kids aboard ship would have none of it. By the fourth day, they insisted on spaghetti for dinner, and the waiters accommodated them with vats of the stuff.

One night Arnoldo decided to occupy our children by filling our water glasses with water and running his finger around the edges to create piercing tones. As Yo Yo Ma and his family sat nearby, I thought, "What must they think of the heathens?" My question was answered during the last night's dinner, when Yo Yo selected the biggest round table in the dining room and filled it with children. He then filled all the water glasses with different levels of water and let the children experiment with musical tones. When Yo Yo ran his finger around his own glass, the tone sounded more magically sonorous than everyone else's.

FIFTEEN

THE LADY WHO FAINTED

by Marilyn L. Garcia

Trouble is only opportunity in work clothes.
—Henry J. Kaiser

I settled in for the flight home and surveyed the other passengers in the plane. Mostly nondescript travelers in slacks and t-shirts, probably returning from business trips. No kids to disrupt the take-off with their wails. Across the way, an elderly woman in a brocade jacket, accompanied by a younger woman, maybe a niece or a daughter, took her seat.

As the plane taxied down the runway I reviewed my situation. What time was it? How did I feel? When did I eat last? When would they serve food? What was my blood sugar? It hadn't been great lately, but I was working on it. The plane took off in a powerful, pressured, roaring, collective movement into the sky.

The first two hours of the flight were a boring routine. Then, the flight attendant announced over the intercom: "Is there a doctor on board? We have a passenger who is a diabetic who needs assistance." I saw a woman carrying a medical bag make her way up the aisle. She must have been a doctor. I didn't know the downside risks for doctors in stepping forward in this way, so admired her willingness to help. The flight attendant met the doctor in the aisle and they made their way over to the woman, who had fainted.

The flight attendant and the doctor hovered over her, and the doctor took her pulse. The woman began to move her head back and forth, in agony.   I wondered if the doctor had supplies in her bag to treat diabetics. Probably not, I thought, unless she was an endocrinologist or a diabetic herself. So I pressed a button above my seat to summon a flight attendant.

When she came over, I volunteered: "I'm a diabetic and I have a blood sugar test kit the doctor could use to test the lady's blood sugar, if she would like." She consulted the doctor and summoned me to join the medical team. I had the presence of mind to insert a new lancet into the fingertip pricker before joining them.

"Hi. I'm a diabetic and here is my blood sugar testing machine," I volunteered as I handed the doctor the equipment. Together, we stuck the woman's finger and waited for the results. 150.

"That is a bit high but really very good. There is nothing wrong with her blood sugar. Not too high or too low," I advised the doctor, as the woman regained consciousness.

They thanked me and I returned to my seat, pleased that I was of assistance. Then I mused to myself: "I bet my own blood sugar is higher than hers. Right now that lady is in better shape than I am!"

SIXTEEN

THE TRIP I DIDN'T TAKE TO MONGOLIA

by Marilyn L. Garcia

When you travel, remember that a foreign country is not designed to make you comfortable. It is designed to make its own people comfortable.—Clifton Fadiman

D espite claiming to be an international adventurer, I drew the line when it came to going to Mongolia. Marco wanted to go to Mongolia, but I was unsure what such a trip would involve for a diabetic. So I decided to ask my friend, Pam, who had been to Tuva, the now non-existent

country between Mongolia and Tibet which fascinated the Nobel Prize winning physicist Richard
Feynman because Tuva issued triangular stamps
picturing exotic people on horseback. Pam spent
half her time in Tibet, sometimes among the
Kampa warriors in eastern Tibet, which I considered adventurous.

Pam's report was not encouraging: she herself
had looked into going to Mongolia but had found it
to be too "primitive" with very little variety in the
food beyond meat and animal products. That might
have been good news for those on the Atkins diet,
but it was not good news for diabetics. If it was too
primitive for Pam, it was too primitive for me. If I
became ill or lost my medication in the middle of
thousands of miles of steppes, rescue would not be
easy.

I wondered if Mongolia was as medically impov-
erished as Sri Lanka, where, according to a doctor
who had practiced there, doctors determined who
was a diabetic by pouring a urine sample on the
ground. A person was diabetic if the sample
attracted ants due to its sugar content. Or maybe it
was like Nepal: a health care worker who had been
stationed in a rural village there told me that insulin
dependency there was a "death sentence," so people
who could, moved away.

My intuitions have been partially confirmed. A

recent message in an internet chat room for diabetics came from a woman from Mongolia. She reported that her father-in-law who lived in Mongolia died at the age of 49 because of a lack of affordable medical supplies in the country.

Although I did not go to Mongolia, my husband and son did. They took a fully packed first-aid kit and basic food supplies with them. I have included Marco's story about his trip because not many of us will ever go to Mongolia, and it invites suggestions about how to plan to go to out-of-the-way places.

MONGOLIA

By Marco Beltrán

Mongolia has always conjured up the idea of an exotic and distant land that hasn't developed since the middles ages. Because of the Soviet era, this is not the exact truth. Cities the size of Seattle (well, one or two of them) stand in the middle of an otherwise barren land. In the capital city of Ulaan Baatar, the sky is filled with the noise of automobiles and smoke from coal burning power plants. Outside the major cities, the landscape is dotted with small communities made up of several houses of *gers*. A *ger* is a tent made out of canvas and felt about the size of a room. Despite the urbanization, one occasionally sees a camel in the middle of town, horses and goats gather in the outskirts of the cities, and many animals (especially horses) dot the countryside. Because of this, the land and traditions of this country have not been spoiled.

The idea of a trip to Mongolia dawned on me when I was writing a report on China for my history class. While researching China, I learned about the Mongolian empire and became fascinated with it. I thought we should plan a trip there. My mom and sister didn't want to go, so it was just me and my dad. After months of planning and with the assistance of a travel agent in Hong Kong, we had our final trip itinerary.

Our journey began when we landed in Ulaan Baatar, nine hours late because our flight was delayed due to Siberian winds that would have made it difficult to land. My dad and I ate a lot of free meals in the Beijing airport while we waited to take off. When we finally arrived in Mongolia and met our guide and driver (a benefit of proper planning), we saw a deserted landscape around us. It looked similar to some parts of Utah or the Imperial Valley in California. Red rolling hills were on the sides of us. When we passed the top of a hill and began heading down to Ulaan Baatar, we could see the lights of the city in darkness. It was a medium sized city nestled between several mountains. There were several towers on the outer parts of the city puffing out smoke from the coal plants. Our car trip ended at the Bayangol Hotel. The two towers that make up the hotel stand out from the background. We got to our room which was pretty nice but smaller than most for the price.

The next morning began with breakfast at the restaurant downstairs. The food was good but the flies landing on the sausage made you want to have eggs. We met with our guide, Sergelin, got our stuff, and were off. Sergelin spoke English, Russian, Mongolian and Japanese. I realized we were in an isolated country when Sergelin and all the other Mongolians we met on the trip thought that the braces on my teeth were jewelry.

The destination of the day was Karakorum. Karakorum was the ancient Mongolian capital. The road to Karakorum was very scenic with all of the animals and horse riders. We stopped for lunch at a tourist *ger* camp. We started with a strange looking fish course that came with cheese. It was the whole fish, kind of like sardines, with cheese. Our driver dived right into it, but we were reluctant to have any. After a few questions, my dad and I tried it. It was good. The soup course was delicious and the main course of beef, purple cabbage, and corn was good too.

After the break, we headed off to the monastery. It was surrounded with 108 stupas, which are Buddhist prayer towers, each about 40 feet tall. Not much of the monastery is left since the Stalinist purges of the thirties. There are several temples left which are very beautifully decorated. The charge for photos and videos was an appalling nine dollars. If you have enough money to spare and do pay the photo charge, please don't take photos inside the temples. It can be disrespectful and wear away the wall paint.

After a full day, we returned to Ulaan Baatar. The next morning started with breakfast at the hotel. We then left for an overnight trip to Terelj. Terelj is a national park in central Mongolia that is definitely worth a visit. There are stunning rock formations, one of which looks remarkably similar to a man reading a book and the most famous of which looks like a turtle. After passing through forty miles of dessert, and a few miles of national park, we got to our destination, a *ger* camp run by Juulchin, which is an international travel company. It looks like someone set up a *ger* camp in a parking lot, but that kept most of the bugs away. If you are still worried about bugs, you can stay in the hotel nearby. If you stay at the camp you may be visited by some curious animals such as yaks and cows. You also may have a visit by some dogs who live with nomads nearby. We had a small black dog crawl under the felt wall of our *ger* and wake us up in the middle of the night. In the evening, we visited a nomadic family living nearby. They were very generous. They offered us many different foods and their salty tea. We gave them some American foods like snack crackers. After about an hour, we left for our *ger* camp and went to sleep.

The next morning, we took some pictures of the red sky and left. The road out was scenic, but on one picture stop, we stopped in the middle of a swarm of flies and bees. After we got back to Ulaan Baatar, we spent the rest of the day resting. The next day we would go to the Siberian border. When I say the Siberian border, I am not exaggerating to make this report better. Our destination was less than sixty miles to the border with Russia, the magnificent Hovsgol Nuur, an alpine lake about seventy miles long running north and south, and about twenty miles east and west. It is surrounded by mountains and has one island in the middle. The lake contains two percent of the world's freshwater and is the second largest lake in Mongolia.

Back in Ulaan Baatar for our trip to the lake, we got to the airport with Sergelin. After a few minutes, a bus arrived to take us to the plane out in the airfield. The plane was an ancient and decrepit Antonov 30 Soviet-made plane. It had two propellers, about five crew members, and could seat about eighty. They had sold twice as many tickets as there were seats, so we had to run to the plane when it opened its doors to make sure we got on. The cabin was extremely hot on the inside. In addition to us passengers, the plane carried dead livestock in the back. After about ten minutes, we were served a melted chocolate candy, and a glass of an orange flavored drink. The plane flew low enough so that we could make out the *gers* on the landscape that was becoming greener and greener. After about an hour and fifteen minutes, the plane landed at the Muren dirt air strip on the second bounce. It seemed like they were doing construction outside of the one terminal, but it was probably just piping for proper plumbing. (Pray that at that point you don't have to go to the bathroom. You'll find out once you see them.)

The drive from the airport to the lake was going to be four hours, and we were going to ride in a jeep. We left the airport driveway and noticed everyone was going left, but we were going right. We also noticed that all the inside walls of the jeep were padded. A few minutes later, we found out that this was because the road was deplorable and had a bump every second. We saw many animals on the way, including goats, sheep, horses and yaks. At one point the road became so bumpy that our driver drove off the road and through the fields because the fields were less bumpy than the road.

After a few hours, we arrived at the park entrance. We had lost our permit to enter the park, but luckily Sergelin knew the gatekeeper from high school, so he gave us a new one. There were many dried up river beds that we had to cross, and lots of potholes, but we survived thanks to the padded jeep walls. Eventually, we got to an area thick with trees.

After reaching where the road goes to the top of the mountain, we saw our first glimpse of the lake. It was very cloudy, foggy and raining, so we couldn't see that much of the lake, but it still looked nice. We stayed at a *ger* camp in the town of Toilogt which is visible on a map, but in real life is nowhere to be seen. It is about twenty miles north of the southern-most part of the lake on the western shore. We finally arrived there in drenching rain. Our *ger* had a wooden floor, stove, dresser, and three beds. We went to dinner which warmed us up, and turned in for the night a little later.

The next day, I tried horse riding. Even though it was really foggy and drizzling, it was still fun. We took a ride around a small lake, or large pond near the lake. We saw lots of yaks. These yaks may also come into the *ger* camp joined by wandering cows. Skipping rocks is also something fun to do at the lake. Be careful that you don't take them from the piles of rocks, which are shamanist relics. Hiking, kayaking, and fishing are also fun things to do here. For fishing you will need a special permit.

On our way back to Muren, we stopped to visit with some Tsaatan people. The Tsaatan people are a tribe whose life revolves around the reindeer. They use it for meat, milk and hides. Unlike most Mongolians, the Tsaatan people (about 300) live in tepees made out of reindeer hides. We didn't get a chance to see the inside their tepee, or even get close to it, but we were able to have a short conversation with them.

When we returned to Muren, we were about an hour early so we had lunch at a restaurant run by the travel company Juulchin. After that, we tried a famous Mongolian drink known as Airag. Airag is fermented mare's milk that is usually served in a leather bag. I was sorry I tried it. It had a tangy, almost fruity flavor. Ten minutes later, my stomach was bouncing up and down like people at a rock concert.

We finally flew back to Ulaan Baatar. Ulaan Baatar was founded in 1758 and called the City of Felt because of the hats made of felt and felt *gers*. It became the capital of Mongolia in 1911 and received its current name, Ulaan Baatar (Red Hero), in 1924. Today, the Mongolian capital has a gray cloud of pollution hanging over it made by a few power stations on the outskirts of the city. There are still many *ger* suburbs where most of the people in the city live. Because of communist urbanization, there are a number of apartment complexes. We also saw many cranes erecting new complexes.

As before, we were staying in the Bayangol Hotel. Our morning began with a trip to the Zaisan memorial on the summit of a nearby mountain on the outskirts of the city. The Zaisan memorial is dedicated to the Mongolians and Russians who died in wars. It has very interesting layout. After a climb of

400 steps, there is a concrete circle about twenty feet off the ground supported by concrete posts and a very interesting spire. The inside of the circle is made of tiles and tells the history of the great conflicts, beginning with the Russian revolution of 1917 and ending with the cosmonauts.

We then stopped at a natural history museum which had exhibits on cavemen and Genghis Khaan. Surprisingly enough, we found an Internet café. After this, we saw Sukhbaatar Square which is dedicated to the heroic officer of the Mongolian army who participated in the fight against the White Russian troops, and led Mongolia before he was killed, probably by Stalin.

Our final stop was a Mongolian cultural show. The first part of the show was a group of dancers, then a band with many exotic instruments including the horse-headed fiddle known as the morin khuur. Our favorite part of the show was the contortionist act. The girls were only seven or eight years of age and trained every day. They can bend their bodies in unimaginable ways. You have to see it to believe it. The final act was a Tsam dance. Tsam dances are dances that tell stories with the dancers wearing very interesting masks. At the end of the show, you can buy recordings of the music but the quality may not be so good. For dinner, we went to a Korean restaurant which had great food and was called the Genghis Khaan restaurant. This was probably the best restaurant for five thousand miles, and the only one without any flies. Our Mongolian journey ended the next morning when we left for the airport to return to Beijing.

SEVENTEEN

THE ER

by Louis Acosta, M.D., as told by Marilyn L. Garcia

What does not destroy me, makes me stronger.
—Friedrich Nietzsche

I've been an emergency room physician for 30 years. I also worked with a company that provided medical assistance to travelers all over the world; my job was to oversee the international travelers who were visiting the United States. Although I arranged to send some very sick people back to their home countries, diabetes is not a disease that ever required such a drastic remedy on my watch. That was more likely to happen when someone sustained severe trauma such as multiple broken bones—Japanese tourists who visited the Grand Canyon sometimes fell off its cliffs.

A diabetic usually shows up in ER when he or she is brought in by a relative or the police because of erratic behavior. It's usually caused by low blood sugar, but sometimes high blood sugar. If I know someone is a diabetic, or if I suspect that he is, I usually blast him with D50 because the chances are it's low blood sugar. The D stands for dextrose—sugar, and the 50 stands for 50% dextrose in 50 cubic centimeters of solution. If a diabetic comes in with exteremely high blood sugar, I hook him or her up to an intravenous injection of saline solution to wash the sugar out, and give an injection of rapid-acting insulin based on an endocrinologist's instructions.

It's very important to wear some type of identification indicating you are a diabetic, because we don't always figure it out. There is a widely circulated story about a Black movie producer who was stopped for erratic driving by the police, known in Los Angeles as the LAPD, because they thought he was drunk, or "DUI," driving under the influence. Despite LAPD procedures requiring the police to take such people to the nearest ER, they decided to take things into their own hands. They took him to the county hospital, where indigents sometimes wait for days to be seen. Sure enough, the movie producer languished without attention for more than 24 hours. Eventually a doctor examined him and determined he was a diabetic who had been suffering from low blood sugar, but he was *not* indigent.

The other diabetic case I remember was the man who was brought into ER in an almost comatose condition. I asked his relative if he was a diabetic and she insisted he wasn't. I was baffled. His symptoms and behavior indicated a low blood sugar condition. So I tested his blood sugar level anyway and, sure enough, it was less than 10!! Out came the D50 real quick! But how could this be? It turned out the old man had been taking diabetic pills a friend had given him under the bizarre belief the pills would cure some of his other ailments. This occurred before viagra had been developed. The pills, which lower blood sugar over a longer time than insulin, had lowered his blood sugar drastically.

PART
TWO

TIPS

ONE

BASIC PLANNING AND TIME CHANGES

THE FIRST BIG TRIP

1. It is generally advised to see your health care professional 4 to 6 weeks before you plan to leave to determine if you are in good health to go, obtain prescriptions for insulin, syringes, pills and blood testing supplies, and have a tetanus booster. Experienced travelers often travel with less advance planning time.

2. Wear some form(s) of medical identification (ID)—bracelet, necklace and/or card—indicating you are a diabetic. Medic Alert sells bracelets, pendants and cards (1-800-825-3785; www.medicalert.org), Lauren's Hope sells medical ID jewelry (www.laurenshope.com), and the magazines listed in Part III (Bibliography and Additional Information) advertise many ID products.

3. If your ID has an emergency telephone number on it, make sure it includes a telephone number that has an area code that is not an 800 number so that it can be called from abroad. When making international telephone calls, you need to use a coun-

try code at the beginning of the number. The county code to call to the United States is 1.

4. Wear comfortable shoes and socks without bumps or holes, and take especially good care of your feet.

5. See Part II (Chapter 8—Packing Medications and Supplies) for packing suggestions.

6. You should obtain a doctor's letter on his or her letterhead stating: (i) you have diabetes, (ii) you must carry your medical supplies with you at all times, and (iii) your treatment and any other medications you take. See Chapter 11 for the reason to have a cover letter in the native language. A few countries, such as Indonesia, require a letter of introduction verified by the Consulate staff if you visit their country.

7. Diabetics who travel frequently (see Chapter 2) may wish to obtain undated doctor's letters and undated prescriptions once each year to use throughout the year.

8. The Bureau of Consular Affairs of the U.S. State Department provides information for U.S. citizens regarding traveling abroad, including passport and visa information, locating U.S. embassies, and health bulletins, at www.travel.state.gov.

9. The International Association for Medical Assistance to Travellers (IAMAT), 417 Center Street, Lewiston, New York 14092; (716) 754-4883; www.iamat.org, can provide a list of western-trained English-speaking doctors in various countries who will treat members of the organization; a small donation is encouraged for membership. The association also provides information on climate, food and sanitary conditions in various countries.

ADJUSTING TO TIME CHANGES

1. See Part II (Chapters 2 and 3—Traveling With a Pump) for suggestions on how to adjust an insulin pump for time changes.

2. Diabetics who take pills to control their diabetes should discuss with their health care professional how to deal with time changes: (i) whether the times for taking the pills should be changed, (ii) whether to take a pill only with a meal, and (iii) whether to take a pill even if a meal is skipped. Generally, pills classified as sulfonylureas and meglithnides reduce blood sugar and should be taken only with a meal or snack. See Part III (Terms and Definitions Used in This Book) for the types of pills available and how they work.

3. If you take insulin, show your travel itinerary to your health care professional so that he or she can advise you on adjustments to your medication schedule. When I travel across 3 time zones or less, I do not adjust my insulin schedule other than to take my next dose of intermediate/long acting insulin at the earlier or later time once I reach my destination. The ways I have adjusted my insulin schedule on airplane flights across more time zones are below. My goal on the day of travel has to prevent ketoacidosis and low blood sugar.

INTERMEDIATE WITH RAPID/SHORT-ACTING INSULIN CHANGES

When I took intermediate-acting insulin and traveled across more than 3 time zones, I took my typical insulin regimen before I left, adjusted during the trip (if it was lengthy), and began taking insulin based on the destination time when I arrived at my destination. When a long airplane trip added many hours (e.g., 8 or 10 hours) to my day (going west), I took a greater number of rapid/short-acting insulin shots (one for each 4-hour interval) and covered each dose by eating a snack or meal. I also took a dose of intermediate-acting insulin (lente or NPH) to cover the extra 8 to 10 hour time interval.

If the time extension was less (say, 5 or 6 hours), I covered the extra time interval only with a dose of rapid/short acting insulin (and maybe a little extra since the intermediate-acting insulin would have run out), and took the next dose of intermediate-acting insulin based on my destination time after I arrived. I tested my blood sugar regularly to make sure I was OK.

If I was going to lose a significant number of hours (going east), I skipped one of the intermediate-acting doses, and covered each 4-hour time interval with a dose of rapid/short-acting insulin and a snack or meal with each dose. I tested my blood sugar regularly to make sure I was OK.

LONG-ACTING WITH RAPID/SHORT-ACTING INSULIN CHANGES

I now take long-acting insulin that has no peaking time (Lantus) at the same time each day (late evening) instead of intermediate-acting insulin. When I take a long airplane trip that will add 8 to 10 hours (going west) to my day, I take my normal doses on the day I leave, and the long-acting insulin at the normal late evening time based on the time at my place of departure (even if I'm then on the airplane). I then deal with the extra hours during the trip by taking successive doses of rapid/short-acting insulin each 4 hours, along with a meal or snack. Because the long-acting insulin may run out during the added hours, my dose of rapid/short-acting insulin might be slightly higher than my typical dose during the added hours. I test my blood sugar regularly to make sure I am OK.

When I take a long airplane trip that will shorten my day by 8 or 10 hours (going east), I take my normal doses on the day I leave, including the long-acting insulin at the normal late evening time (during my travel/flight) based on the time at my place of departure. I take rapid/short-acting insulin with each meal or snack during travel, and take my next dose of long-acting insulin at the late evening time based on the local time of my destination after I arrive, even though it has not been a full 24 hours since my last long-acting dose. I test my blood sugar regularly to make sure I am OK.

TRAVELING WITH A PUMP

WILD IN CALIFORNIA AND SLEEPING AROUND

1. Take twice as much medicine and equipment as you think you will need, including syringes, even if you use a pump. If your pump uses only rapid-acting insulin, also take some intermediate-acting or long-acting insulin to use with the syringes if the pump breaks down.

2. Take extra batteries and make sure the batteries come from multiple batches. Take the pump user manual.

3. Arrive at the airport in advance of the standard suggested time to allow extra time for airport screening with your pump.

4. The Transportation Security Administration (TSA) guidelines state that you should notify screeners at the security checkpoint that you are wearing a pump and cannot go through a metal detector or be hand-wanded. However, pump manufacturers have indicated that insulin pumps can operate near sources of electrostatic and elec-tromagnetic interference, including airport secu-

rity systems. You may nevertheless request a visual inspection and advise the screener that the pump cannot be removed because it is connected to you via a catheter.

5. The TSA guidelines state that pumps and supplies must be accompanied by insulin and have professionally-printed labels identifying the medication or manufacturer's name or pharmacy. See Part II (Chapter 11—Dealing with Airport Security) for more information on the TSA guidelines.

6. It is essential that you have the telephone numbers for the pump manufacturer and the provider of your pump supplies. If you are going out of the country, make sure you have the pump manufacturer's telephone number in the destination country or, at the very least, have the telephone numbers with a specific U.S. area code. The 800 numbers might not work from overseas. Contact information for pump manufacturers now is:

- Amigo Pump - Nipro Diabetes Systems: 1-888-651-7867; 1-954-435-5665
- Animas IR 1200 Pump-Animas Corporation: 1-877-937-7867; 1-610-644-8990; www.animascorp.com

- DANA Diabecare II Pump-DANA Diabecare USA: 1-866-342-2322; www.theinsulinpump.com
- Deltec CozMore Insulin Technology System-Smith Medical MD, Inc.: 1-800-999-1264; www.delteccozmo.com
- Disetronic Pump - Disetronic Medical System: 1-800-280-7801; www.disetronic-usa.com
- Medtronic Minimed 512/712 Pumps-Medtronic Minimed: 1-800-646-4633

Because there are many suppliers of pump supplies, their contact information is not listed here, but it is essential that you also have contact information on the company providing your supplies.

7. If you are changing time zones, set the insulin pump clock to the destination time during the trip or when you arrive. Set the basal rate to the daytime rate while you are traveling. When you arrive at your destination, adjust the basal rates to the multiple daytime rates based on the destination time. As always, bolus for meals and high blood sugar.

Sources for pump manufacturers: *Diabetes Forecast*, January 2005; *Diabetes Health*, January 2005. Source for pump time adjustment: Kruger, Davida F., *The Diabetes Travel Guide*, American Diabetes Association (2000).

FOUR

BUYING MEDICATIONS AND SUPPLIES IN OTHER COUNTRIES

WE CAN'T SPEAK FRENCH

1. It is very easy for you, your pharmacist or your health care professional to call the customer service representatives of the manufacturers of the insulins or other medications you use or might use. Your pharmacist will have their numbers. Their 800 numbers usually do not work from overseas, so calling the manufacturers before you leave will not only be easier, it saves money. However, you probably won't lose your insulin, so you may not wish to call ahead of time, and only take the contact information with you (and/or leave it with a friend at home) to use if you lose your insulin. The telephone numbers of insulin manufacturers are:

- Aventis Pharmaceuticals: 1-800-633-1610; 1-800-981-2491; 1-908-243-6000
- Eli Lilly and Company: 1-800-545-5979; 1-317-276-2000
- Novo Nordisk: 1-800-727-6500; 1-609-987-5800

You should determine if your type of insulin is readily available in the country where you are going. If it is, ask for both the name (or identification number) and the concentration (U-40 or U-100) used there.

2. If your type and/or brand of insulin is not readily available, you should ask your health care professional if you could substitute another type and/or brand of insulin, and the health care professional should set out a regimen using the substitute types and brands of insulin. This might be the case if you would have to use NPH instead of long-acting insulin which may not yet be available in as many countries as other brands.

3. You may wish to convert the number of units you use, based on a U-100 concentration, to the number of units you should take if you have to take insulin with a different concentration, so that you will not have to purchase new syringes if you lose your insulin. Also convert the other way to deal with losing your syringes. See Part III (Conversion Formulas). That way you won't have to make any calculations when you are jet lagged or under the stress of dealing with new insulin in a foreign country. I remember the time that, jet-lagged, I converted dollars into French francs the wrong way and ended up paying a *lot* more than I should

have for cab fare—but that's another story.

4. Many countries do not require a prescription to purchase insulin, syringes, or other supplies, but you should obtain prescriptions for these anyway, including substitutes (only if your health care professional approves) if your type of insulin is not commonly available, based on the names and brands used in your destination country.

5. If you do not have all of the necessary information to purchase insulin while aboard, insulin manufacturers have 24-hour customer service lines, and you should call the telephone number that is *not* an 800 number.

6. I usually take a backup blood sugar testing meter with me in case my meter breaks or gets lost. The meters aren't expensive; the manufacturers reap their rewards selling tests strips. But if you don't want to incur the expense of purchasing another meter ahead of time, you can take a bottle of visually-read strips for blood sugar testing.

7. The customer service representatives of the manufacturers of your blood sugar testing meter can provide information on what countries carry their products and the contact information of their distributors in those countries. The customer service

representatives will also be able to give you their contact telephone numbers that are not 800 numbers to use to contact them when you are overseas; they might be able to ship a new meter if you break or lose your meter while abroad. The manufacturers of blood sugar testing meters and their telephone contact information are:

- Abbott Diabetes Care (Freestyle meters): 1-800-527-3339; 1-888-522-5226
- Bayer HealthCare, LLC (Ascensia meters): 1-800-348-8100
- BD: 1-888-232-2737
- Home Diagnostics: 1-800-342-7226; 1-954-677-9201
- Hypoguard USA, Inc.: 1-800-818-8877; 1-952-646-3200
- Lifescan, Inc. (One Touch meters): 1-800-227-8862; 408-263-9789
- QuesStar Medical, Inc. (Focus meters): 1-800-525-6718; 1-952-941-7345
- Roche Diagnostics (Accu-Chek meters): 1-800-858-8072

8. If you obtain a blood sugar meter in another country, keep in mind that the system for measuring blood sugar levels may be different than in the United States. See Part III (Conversion Formulas) for more information.

9. Diabetic pills require prescriptions, and there are many types of pills and brands. If you lose your pills while you are traveling, you should go to a hospital or seek other medical assistance to best determine how to obtain comparable pills.

Sources for insulin and meter manufacturers/distributors: *Diabetes Forecast*, January 2005; *Diabetes Health*, January 2005.

FIVE

IMMUNIZATIONS

GOOD KARMA

Travel health clinics and doctors who specialize in travel medicine can advise you on what immunizations are necessary or recommended for particular countries. The more exotic the country, the more likely special immunizations will be required. Some immunizations must be taken in a series over several weeks or months, so be sure and look into this in plenty of time. The Center for Disease Control also provides this information at (404) 332-4555 or www.cdc.gov., as does IAMAT at (716) 754-4883; www.iamat.org.

SIX

EXERCISE

1. If you will be exercising more than usual you must test your blood sugar more often. Be sure to have candy, glucose tablets, or sugar with you to deal with low blood sugar levels. If you know you will be getting a significant amount of exercise, you may want to eat some additional carbohydrate/protein, such as fruit and cheese, yogurt, or a peanut butter cracker, before you begin.

2. If you do not have candy, sugar, or other snacks available when you are suffering from low blood sugar, another remedy available all over the world is 1/2 can (4-6 oz.) of regular (not diet or Lite) soda, which can be used to treat low blood sugar, according to the *American Diabetes Association's Complete Guide to Diabetes, Third Edition* (2000). I have even seen pictures of Pepsi logos in English on the Inca Trail in Peru and in Dubrovnik, Croatia.

3. Remember that exercise can lower your blood sugar for several hours and even into the next day.

4. Contributors to this book found that if they exercised for a significant portion of the day, it was necessary to reduce insulin intake by about 10%. If the increased exercise and the 10% reduction still resulted in low blood sugars, it was necessary to reduce insulin intake by an additional 10% to 20%.

5. When I took short-acting or intermediate-acting insulin, which peaks several hours after injection, and planned to exercise for only part of the day, I tried to avoid exercising at the time my insulin peaked. See Part III (Terms and Definitions Used in This Book) for peaking times for different insulins.

6. For diabetics who take pills, adjusting medications due to additional exercise is more complicated than for those taking insulin because many types of pills do not lower blood sugar levels in the short run. Diabetics who take pills should consult their health care professionals to obtain specific information about what to do if they will be increasing their exercise regimen.

7. If you will be doing something particularly challenging—scuba diving, sky diving, or mountain climbing, for example—you *must* see your health care professional to understand all the precautions necessary to do it safely.

8. Set out below are some types of exercise described in this book and the calories burned each hour.

HIKING CROSS COUNTRY
Hiking in Tuscany
Inca Trail to Machu Pichu in Peru
(24.6 miles, taking 4 days)
China's Great Wall from Jinshanling to Simatai
(10 km, taking 4 hours)
354 calories per hour by 130 lb. person
422 calories per hour by 155 lb. person

STAIR CLIMBING
Eiffel Tower in Paris (total of 1700 steps)
Torre del Mangia (400 steps) in Siena, Italy
472 calories per hour by 130 lb person
563 calories per hour by 155 lb. person

BICYCLING
(moderate effort)
In China to the Ming Tombs
590 calories per hour by 130 lb. person
704 calories per hour by 155 pound person

CITY WALKING
Paris, Villages in Tuscany
207 calories per hour by 130 lb. person
246 calories per hour by 155 lb. person

Source for calorie counts: www.nutristrategy.com/activitylist.html. This website has calorie counts for many types of exercise.

SEVEN

STORING INSULIN

THE TRAIN TRIP

1. When booking a hotel room or other lodging, try to book a room with a mini-refrigerator to store insulin. If not, ask to store it in a central refrigerator.

2. Test strips for your blood sugar meter should always be kept at room temperature—out of direct sunlight and never in a refrigerator.

3. Diabetics should already know the storing requirements for the insulin they use, so the information here may be unnecessary. Nevertheless, you can ask your pharmacist, the insulin manufacturer, or your health care professional which, if any, of your insulin must be chilled. The instructions with each box of insulin also provide this information. It makes a difference if a vial has or has not yet been used or opened. It is better to keep insulin bottles in the refrigerator (but never the freezer) even if chilling is not necessary.

4. Even if it is not chilled, insulin should not be stored at temperatures below 40 degrees Farenheit or above 86 degrees Farenheit. Most

other countries use the centigrade scale for temperatures: 40 degrees Farenheit is 5 degrees centigrade, and 86 degrees Farenheit is 30 degrees centigrade. The manufacturer of Novo Nordisk suggests a maximum of 77 degrees Farenheit, 25 degrees centigrade. You should purchase new insulin if it is subject to temperatures beyond this range, unless your health care provider advises otherwise.

5. You may use a bottle of insulin for up to 30 day if it has been opened and has been at room temperature. On the bottle write the date you first began to use it and the date it should be discarded. A bottle of insulin should always be discarded if the insulin changes it appearance (discolored, cloudy, large particles in the liquid).

6. If you will use prefilled insulin pens and cartridges, confirm how long they may last at room temperature and whether they should be chilled. Generally, pens/cartridges with Regular and Humalog can be stored at room temperature (less than 77 dgrees Farenheit for 30 days; prefilled pens/cartridges containing NPH or a 70/30 blend can be stored at room temperature for 7 days; pens with a 75/25 blend can be stored at room temperature for 10 days.

7. Your life may be a lot simpler if you purchase a cold gel pack in which to carry your insulin. Cool packs are available from the following companies, and others:
   - Apothecary Products—1-800-328-2742; 1-952-890-1940
   - FRIO Cooling Products—011-44-01437-741700; info@frio.us.com
   - Medicool, Inc.—1-800-433-2469; 1-310-782-2200; www.medicool.com

Source for cool pack manufacturers/distributors: *Diabetes Forecast*, January 2005.

EIGHT

PACKING MEDICATIONS AND SUPPLIES

CONNECTING FLIGHTS

1. Carry essentials—toothbrush and the like, and a change of clothes—in your carry-on bag in case your checked luggage gets lost.

2. Take twice as much of your medications and supplies as you will need, including additional batteries for all equipment because special batteries can be difficult to obtain.

3. If you are traveling with another person, divide up your medications and supplies between the two of you, after you have gone through security, so you have what you will need if your purse or pouch is lost or stolen.

4. If security guards decide your carry-on is too big, it will be checked into the cargo hold, so put your medications, supplies and other essentials, such as food, in a small zippered pocket bag to pull out and take onto the airplane if your carry-on is checked.

5. Do not pack your medications or supplies (especially if they are your *only* medications and supplies) in your checked luggage. Nevertheless, some people who travel alone suggest packing *back up* medications and supplies in checked luggage in order to deal with the unlikely event that your primary medications and supplies are confiscated by security personnel.

6. If you pack insulin in your checked luggage, put it in an insulated container to protect it from the extreme cold of the cargo hold, as well as excessive heat.

NINE

MEAL SCHEDULING

SPANISH DINNER TIME

Today diabetics are accustomed to being out and about, so adjusting to variations in meal offerings and schedules should be very familiar to diabetics. But some countries have different meal customs that may require extra planning and thought.

1. Some countries, such as Spain and Italy, have only a light continental breakfast, so diabetics may have to cut down on their rapid-acting or short-acting insulin at breakfast.

2. People in some countries, such as Spain, Greece and certain Latin American countries, begin dinner late by United States standards, about 10 p.m. Others in countries such as Italy have a large main meal at midday. You should research the meal customs of the country where you are going. In most places you probably can eat at the times you are accustomed, but the key is to adapt. You should consult your health care professional to determine how to adjust your medication for schedule and diet changes.

3. For those who take intermediate-acting insulin that peaks, such as NPH or lente, a late afternoon snack is a must to tide you over until a late dinner.

4. For those who take a long-acting insulin with no peaking time, have an insulin pump, or take oral medication geared to eating times, changes may have a minimum impact on how you take your medication.

5. Dr. Isabelle, one of our hosts during the trip to Spain, advises that a diabetic should focus on eating carbohydrate foods and be aware of the types of carbohydrates in a meal. The way food is cooked makes a difference: carbohydrates that are overcooked are absorbed more rapidly, so Italian cooking is great because the pasta is cooked *al dente* (cooked enough to retain a somewhat firm texture), but Spanish *paella*, which is practically "fried rice," is absorbed quickly and extra rapid/short-acting insulin is necessary. No wonder the well-cooked Chinese noodles I ate during my first trip caused my blood sugar to shoot through the roof (Chapter 1—The First Big Trip). When in doubt, Dr. Isabelle advises that it is better to eat foods that will slow the absorption of the carbohydrates, such as high fiber foods like lentils and chick peas.

6. Most diabetics who are in good control can have alcoholic beverages, such as wine or distilled spirits, but alcoholic beverages can significantly lower blood sugar levels. Diabetics who use sulfonylureas pills or insulin should drink alcohol only with a snack or meal. You should consult your health care professional regarding the effects alcohol has on any other medication you are taking and whether you can have alcoholic beverages while taking such medication.

TEN

ADMINISTERING MEDICA-TION ON THE ROAD

TURBULENCE

1. An aisle seat in the airplane permits you to more easily get up to stretch your legs, go to the restroom for medications, or request special assistance from a flight attendant.

2. You can minimize the problem of turbulence when you take an insulin injection on an airplane by using insulin pens with pre-filled cartridges available at your pharmacy. No refrigeration is generally required for one week after first use. The pens require pen needles also available at your pharmacy. Insulin pens and/or supplies may require a prescription. Some of the pens available are listed below.

   - Autopen (Owen Mumford, Inc.)
   - Disetronic Pen (Disetronic Medical Systems)
   - Humalog Pen (Eli Lilly and Company)—these come in pen for a 75-25 mix, 70/30 mix or for one type of insulin
   - Novolog Pens—these come in pens for a 70/30 mix or for one type of insulin

Source for insulin pen manufacturers/distributors: *Diabetes Forecast*, January 2005.

ELEVEN

DEALING WITH AIRPORT SECURITY

The suggestions below are important, but, unlike other contributors to this book, I have never been challenged by airport security for carrying insulin, syringes and other medical supplies with me. Maybe I appear so uncoordinated as to be incapable of carrying out a hostile act!

1. The Federal Transportation Security Administration (TSA) established guidelines for diabetic travel (see www.tsa.gov). Keep in mind that these are only guidelines (not rules, which must be followed) and they apply to U.S. domestic flights only. The TSA guidelines suggest that you notify your security screener that you are a diabetic and are carrying supplies with you. The guidelines allow the following supplies and equipment to be kept with you after they have been screened, provided that they are labeled to be identifiable:

- Insulin and insulin-loaded dispensing products (vials or box of individual vials, jet injectors, pens, infusors, and pre-loaded syringes), which

must be clearly identified and labeled, with prescriptions
- Unlimited number of unused syringes when accompanied by insulin or other injectable medication
- Lancets, blood sugar meters, test strips, alcohol swabs, and meter testing solution
- Insulin pump and pump supplies (cleaning agents, infusion kit, catheter and needles)
- Glucagon emergency kit
- Urine ketone test strips
- Unlimited number of used syringes when in sharps disposal container or similar hard-surface container

2. The TSA guidelines provide that if you do not wish to have your supplies run through the x-ray screener, you may request a visual inspection of your insulin and supplies. If you wish to do so, the following TSA guidelines apply:

- Medications and supplies should be clearly labeled and kept in a separate pouch
- You must request the visual inspection before the screening process begins and you must hand your medication pouch/bag to the screener

- To prevent contamination or damage, you will be required to display, handle and repack the medication and supplies during the visual screening
- Any medication or other supplies that cannot be cleared visually must be submitted for x-ray screening; otherwise, you will not be allowed to carry them with you

3. The TSA guidelines suggest that you advise screeners if you are experiencing low blood sugar and need assistance.

4. The TSA guidelines for insulin pumps are in Part II (Chapters 2 and 3—Traveling With a Pump).

5. The TSA guidelines apply only to security inspections in the United States, although the TSA guidelines are good suggestions to follow in other countries. If you are going to another country, you should have prescriptions for your medications and supplies, and a letter from your doctor stating that you are a diabetic and must keep your medications and supplies with you at all times. If there is a possibility that you will be faced with security situations where the screeners or guards do not speak English, you may want to have a cover letter in the native language (or a language likely to be

spoken there, such as French in some African countries) briefly explaining that you are a diabetic and must keep medications and supplies with you. Sample cover letters in common foreign languages follow. If you would like to obtain a letter in another language, one place to obtain a translation is elcano.bowneglobal.com, which will translate desired phrases from English into many languages, including Arabic, Bosnian, Bulgarian, Polish, Slovenian, Thai and Turkish. See the Tips for Chapter 12 (Language Translations) for more information.

6. The following is suggested text for a cover letter that could be translated into another language.

> Attached is a physician's letter stating that this person is a diabetic and must carry medications and medical supplies with him/her at all times. If there is any question regarding this matter, I respectfully request to consult your supervisor.

Translations of the above paragraph into 8 common languages follow. These pages can be copied or removed from this book and attached to the front of your doctor's letter.

SPANISH

Adjunto carta de doctor declarando que esta persona es diabética y tiene que llevar consigo medicamentos y utensilios médicos con el/ella todo el tiempo. Si hay alguna pregunta tocante a este asunto, pido respetuosamente que consulte con su supervisor.

GERMAN

Anbei ist der Brief eines Arztes der bescheinigt, dass diese Person Diabetiker ist und darer jederzeit Medikamente, medizinische Geraete und Sanitaetsartikel bei sich haben muss. Falls Sie Fragen haben, bitte ich Sie hoeflichst, sich an Iheren Vorgesetzten zu wenden.

ITALIAN

In allegato: dichiarazione firmata da un medico nella quale si dichiara che il soggetto è diabetico e deve costantemente portare con sé medicinali e farmaci. Si prega gentilmente di contattare il proprio supervisore per qualsiasi domanda o dubbio in proposito.

FRENCH

Vous trouverez ci-jointe l'ordonnance d'un médecin indiquant que ce patient est diabétique et doit conserver sur lui tout le temps ses médicaments et ses provisions médicales. Si vous avez des questions à ce sujet, je vous demanderais de consulter votre cadre supérieur.

RUSSIAN

См. прилагаемое письмо врача, подтверждающее, что данный пациент болен диабетом и должен постоянно иметь с собой соответствующие лекарственные препараты и принадлежности. Если у вас возникли какие-либо вопросы, убедительная просьба обратиться к своему руководителю.

JAPANESE

本人が糖尿病であるため、薬や医療関連必需品を常時携帯しなければならないことを記した医者からの手紙を添付してあります。これに関して何か質問等ありましたら、上司の方と相談して頂けますか。

CHINESE

附上的醫師信是告知此人乃糖尿病患
需隨時攜帶藥劑及醫療用品.如有任何
相關問題,我在此懇請您與您的上司
諮詢.

GREEK

Αύτη είναι μία ιατρική πιστοποίηση πού δηλώνει ότι αυτός ο άνθρωπος είναι διαβητικός και πρέπει να φέρει φαρμακευτική αγωγή μαζί του πάντα. Αν υπάρχει καμιά ερώτηση σχετικά μ'αυτό, σας παρακαλώ να συμβουλευτείτε τον επιτηρητή σας.

TWELVE

LANGUAGE TRANSLATIONS

BICYCLING IN THE SHADOW OF THE MING

1. In much of the world, knowledge of English has become a basic skill of modern life comparable with the ability to drive a car or use a personal computer.* When I have traveled, someone who spoke English has usually been available to assist me.

2. An easy way to communicate is to use a nifty little book called *Point It*, Dieter Graf Verlag (ISBN 3-9803130-2-6), available through travel book or map stores. It has pictures of food, hotel, transportation, assistance and other travel essentials, to enable a traveler to communicate just about anything anywhere in the world. My son used *Point It* to order a strawberry milkshake in Estonia. *Point It* includes pictures of sugar, orange juice, soft drinks, a syringe, basic first aid items, a hospital and body organs, including the pancreas. You could assemble your own picture communication package with pictures essential to your care, or supplement the *Point It* book with such pictures.

The Economist, August 4, 2004.

3. The following pages contain some essential diabetic phrases in common foreign languages. Phonetic translations are also provided for French, Russian, Japanese, Chinese and Greek. If you are going to a country with an uncommon primary language, you may wish to determine if many people in the country also speak a more common language and rely on that language as your backup. For example, French is a common second language in many African countries, and Russian is a common second language in Eastern Europe and the Baltic countries. For phrases in other languages, one source is elcano.bowneglobal.com, which translates words and phrases into many languages.

SPANISH

1) Please help me. I have diabetes.

   Por favór ayudenme. Tengo diabetes.

2) May I please have some sugar, candy
   or fruit juice?

   Me puede dar azúcar, dulce, o jugo de fruta?

3) My blood sugar is too low.

   Mi nivél de azúcar está muy bajo.

4) Where is the hospital?

   Donde está el hospital?

5) Where can I buy medicine?

   Donde puedo comprar medicina?

6) I need to buy some insulin.

   Necesito comprar insulina.

7) I need to buy some insulin syringes.

   Necesito comprar jeringas.

GERMAN

1) Please help me. I have diabetes.

   Helfen Sie mir bitte. Ich bin Diabetiker.

2) May I please have some sugar, candy or fruit juice?

   Koennten Sie mir bitte etwas Zucker, eine Suessigkeit, oder einen Fruchsaft geben?

3) My blood sugar is too low.

   Mein Blutzucker ist zu niedrig.

4) Where is the hospital?

   Wo ist das Krankenhaus?

5) Where can I buy medicine?

   Wo kann ich Medikamente kaufen?

6) I need to buy some insulin.

   Ich muss Insulin kaufen.

7) I need to buy some insulin syringes.

   Ich muss Insulin spritzn kaufen.

ITALIAN

1) Please help me. I have diabetes.

   Aiutatemi-ho il diabete.

2) May I please have some sugar, candy
   or fruit juice?

   Per favore potrei avere un po' di zucchero,
   caramella o succo di frutta?

3) My blood sugar is too low.

   Ho la glicemia troppo bassa.

4) Where is the hospital?

   Dov'é l'ospedale?

5) Where can I buy medicine?

   Dov'é posso comprare della medicina?

6) I need to buy insulin for diabetes.

   Devo comprare la insulina per il diabete.

7) I need to buy insulin syringes.

   Mi occorrono le siringhe da insulina.

FRENCH

1) Please help me. I have diabetes.

   Aidez-moi, s'il vous plait.
   Je suis diabétique. (Je fais du diabète.)

   Ayday mwa, see voo play.
   Zhe swee deabeteek (Zhe fay do dezbet.)

2) Can you give me some sugar, candy
   or fruit juice?

   Pouvez-vous me donner du sucre,
   un jus de fruit ou des bonbons?

   Poo vay voo mah donneh do sucreh,
   uh zhoo duh fruee ou day bohboh?

3) My blood sugar is too low.

   Mon taux de sucre dans le sang est trop bas.
   Je suis état d'hypoglycémie.

   Moh tow du sucreh da luh sah eh troh bah.
   Zhe swee ehta dypoglesemee.

4) Where is the hospital?

Où se trouve l'hopital?

Oo suh toove lopital?

5) Where can I buy medicine?

Où puis-je acheter des medicaments?

Oo pwee zhe asheteh day mehdeekamoh?

6) I need to buy some insulin.

J'ai besoin d'acheter de l'insuline.

Zh-ay beswa dosheteh duh lisooleen.

7) I need to buy some insulin syringes.

J'ai besoin d'acheter des seringues
pour l'insuline.

Zh-ay beswa dosheteh day sereenguh
poor lisooleen.

RUSSIAN

1) Please help me. I have diabetes.

   Помогите мне, поЖалуй ста.
   Pomageetye mnye, pazhalsta.

2) May I please have some sugar, candy
   or fruit juice?

   МоЖно сахар, конфета или лимонад.
   Mozhna Sakhar, sok ili limonad.

3) My blood sugar is too low.

   У меня низкий уровень сахара в крови.
   Y meenya nizkii yroven sakhara v krovi.

4) Where is the hospital?

   Где больница?
   Gdye bolnitsa?

5) Where may I buy medicine?

   Где купить лекарство?
   Gdye kupeet lekarstva?

6) I need to buy some insulin.

   Мне надо купить инсулин.
   Mnye nada kupeet insyleen.

7) I need to buy some insulin syringes.

   Мне надо купить шприц для инсулина.
   Mnye nada kupeet shpreets dlya insyleen.

JAPANESE

1) Please help me. I have diabetes.

    私は糖尿病です。助けていただけますか。

    Watashi wa toonyobyoo desu. Tasukete
    itadake masuka?

2) May I please have some sugar, candy or
    fruit juice?

    甘いもの、お菓子か果物ジュースいただ
    けますか。

    Amai mono, okashi ka kudamono jyuusu
    itadake masuka?

3) My blood sugar is too low.

    私の血糖値が下がり過ぎています。

    Watashi no kettoochi ga sagari sugite imasu.

4) Where is the hospital?

    病院は何処ですか。

    Byooin wa doko desuka?

5) Where may I buy medicine?

何処で薬が買えますか。

Doko de kusuri ga kae masuka?

6) I need to buy some insulin.

インスリンを買わなければなりません。
Insulin wo kawa nakereba narimasen

7) I need to buy some insulin syringes.

インスリンの注射針を買わなければなり
ません。
Insulin no chushashin wo kawa nakereba
narimasen?

CHINESE

1) Please help me. I have diabetes.

请 帮 助 我. 我 有 糖 尿 病.

Ching bong tsu woh. Who yoh tong neow been.

2) May I please have some sugar, candy or
fruit juice?

请 给 我 一 些 糖, 糖 果,
或 果 汁. 好 吗 ?

Ching gay woh, iseah tong, tong gwoh, foh,
guo tzh howmah?

3) My blood sugar is too low.

我 的 血 糖 很 低.

Gwoh-duh shay-tong hundee.

4) Where is the hospital?

请 问 医 院 在 那 裹 ?

Ching-woún e-yen tzai-nali?

5) Where may I buy medicine?

请 问 在 那 裹 可 以 买 药 ?

Ching-woún tzai-nali kuryee mai yeou?

6) I need to buy some insulin.

我 需 要 買 些 胰 島 素 藥片 (製劑).

Who shee-yów my shéh ee-tow-sue yow pien.

7) I need to buy some insulin syringes.

我 需 要 買 些 胰 島 素 注 射 針.

Who shee-yów my shéh ee-tow-sue tsoo-sur-tsen.

GREEK

1) Please help me. I have diabetes.

Βοήθησέ με, παρακαλώ. Έχω διαβήτη.

Voytheese me parakalo. Ekho dyaveetee.

2) May I please have some sugar, candy or
    fruit juice?

**Θα ήθελα σας παρακαλώ ζάχαρη, καραμέλες
ή χυμό.**

Tha eethela sas parakalo zakharee, karameles
ee kheemo?

3) My blood sugar is too low.

Έχω χαμηλό σάκχαρο.

Ekho khameelo sakkharo.

4) Where is the hospital?

Που είναι το νοσοκομείο;

Pou eene to nosokomeeo?

5) Where may I buy medicine?

Που μπορώ να αγοράσω φάρμακα;

Pou boro na agoraso farmaka?

6) I need to buy some insulin.

Πρέπει να αγοράσω ινσουλίνη.

Prepei na agoraso insouleenee.

7) I need to buy some insulin syringes.

Πρέπει να αγοράσω σύριγγες ινσουλίνης.

Prepei na agoraso seereenges eensooleenees.

THIRTEEN

CONTACT INFORMATION

WHAT WE LEFT IN PARIS

1. You should take contact information with you, and give this list to your traveling companion in case your copy gets lost:

   - Pharmacy
   - Primary care physician
   - Endocrinologist
   - Telephone numbers for manufacturers of insulins, pump, pump supplies, blood sugar meter, and other medical equipment
   - Hospitals and doctors in the region you visit

2. Also leave all of this information with a contact person at home who would be available by telephone or e-mail on a 24-hour basis whom you can contact if you do not have the information with you. Give your contact person other key information, such as your treatment regimen, formulas for converting to U-40 insulin, etc. See Part III (Conversion Formulas).

3. You may want to carry an additional set of prescriptions in your wallet, separate from your medical supplies.

CRUISES

THE CLIFFS OF SANTORINI

1. Don't assume that your food order will arrive on time. This rule applies in all situations, not just cruises. Better to take your rapid-acting or short-acting medication only when the food arrives.

2. Cruises are a prudent travel option for diabetics: the activities and meals follow regular schedules, and the ships have infirmaries. Your insulin can be stored in the infirmary if your cabin does not have a refrigerator. You should introduce yourself to the medical staff when you first board the ship to inform them that you are a diabetic and give them written information on your medications and treatment. A doctor who works on cruise ships told me that his ships' infirmaries had D-50 and saline solution (see Chapter 17—The ER) and more supplies to conduct medical tests than the emergency room of the hospital where he regularly works, although this might not be true for all cruise ships.

3. Cruises usually offer day excursions off the ships at different ports. For the day trips, you should follow

the basic rules for travel: take a set of all of your medical supplies, your doctor's letter, candy or glucose tablets, snacks, and a bottle of water on each outing. And make sure you leave plenty of time to return to the ship at the end of each excursion.

4. Always wear comfortable shoes and socks without bumps or hole, and take especially good care of your feet.

FIFTEEN

INFORMATION FOR TRAVELING COMPANIONS; AIRPLANE TRAVEL TIPS

THE LADY WHO FAINTED

1. If you are traveling with someone else, your companion should know acceptable blood sugar levels, and how to test your blood sugar and give you glucose tablets (or a glucagon injection if you have this) if you are unable to take care of yourself. Your companion should have copies of your prescriptions, medical regimen, and medical contact information.

2. If the airline serves meals, it should be possible to order a special diabetic meal (I never have) if you do so at least 48 hours in advance. But keep in mind that occasionally these special meals are forgotten, or portions are not what they should be.

3. Today many airlines do not serve meals in economy class, even on long flights. This development forces all passengers to bring their own meals, giving diabetics the opportunity to be part of the mainstream yet tailor carry-on meals to dietary requirements.

4. To keep hydrated in the dry airplane cabin air and minimize the effects of jet lag, drink plenty of liquids before boarding, and drink some non-alcoholic fluid each hour you are in the air.

SIXTEEN

TRAVELING TO OUT OF THE WAY PLACES

THE TRIP I DIDN"T TAKE TO MONGOLIA

Whether another country is developed or undeveloped is a matter of degree. The suggestions here could apply to anywhere you go, but are most essential when you go to undeveloped countries. Review the suggestions and determine the extent to which you should use them on a particular trip.

1. It is essential that you follow all the tips in the other parts of this book when you go to an undeveloped country, including: know doctors, hospitals and clinics in the destination country available to treat you; get all immunizations; and inform fellow travelers that you are a diabetic.

2. Try not to go alone.

3. The web page for the Center for Disease Control provides comprehensive information on health and other travel risks for most countries in the world: www.cdc.gov. The International Association for Medical Assistance to Travellers

(IAMAT) also advises travelers about health risks and diseases world-wide, and immunization requirements for all countries: 716-754-4883; www.iamat.org.

4. You should notify the U.S. Embassy in your destination country that you will be visiting the country and that you are a diabetic. The U.S. State of Department advises all travelers (not just diabetics) to undeveloped countries to register with the State Department before going at travel.state.gov. You should keep the local telephone number of the U.S. Embassy with you, such as writing it on your passport.

5. Ask your doctor how you should take care of yourself for a day or more if you do not have any insulin or other such medication.

6. Research how to ship items to the place where you are going. Some shipping companies do not ship medicine, and some countries do not allow shipments of medicine. The U.S. Postal Service ships to many obscure places that some commercial shippers do not go to. Its Global Priority Mail takes 3 to 5 days: USPS.com; 1-800-275-8777; some post offices have an International Mail Manual with this information. Federal Express

ships to many countries: fedex.com, or 1-800-463-3339. DHL is another international company that ships all over the world: dhl.com, or 1-800-CALL-DHL (1-800-225-5345).

7. Pack lots of non-perishable food items to enable you and your traveling companion to eat for a few days.

8. Prepare a first aid kit for your trip and include as many of the following items as you and your health care professional determine are appropriate:
    - 1" bandage tape
    - bandaids
    - gauze pads (large and small)
    - ABD pads (2 large gauze pads)
    - ace bandages 2" and 3"
    - butterfly tapes
    - aspirin (or comparable) for pain and fever
    - dramamine or scopolamine
        (for motion sickness)
    - antihistamine
        (for allergies and to ease insect bite itch)
    - lopermide or diphenoxylate (diarrhea
        blockers); prochlorperazine or
        metaclopramide
        for nausea and vomiting
    - rehydration mixture

- insect repellant, sunscreen, lip balm
  and eye drops
- calamine lotion; sting relief spray or aloe vera
  (for sunburn or insect bites)
- antifungal cream or powder
- antiseptic
- water purification tablets or iodine
- thermometer (mercury type is prohibited
  by airlines)
- sunscreen
- nasal decongestant
- tweezers, scissors (cannot be carried on
  board the airplane)
- Pepto Bismal
- antibiotics
- medications for colds and coughs
- multivitamins
- extra watch or small travel clock
- Syringes and needles, with doctor's note
  explaining why you have them
  (for injections in countries with
  hygiene problems)

Sources for first aid kit supplies: *Lonely Planet Guides* and
Dr. Louis Acosta.

PART
THREE

ADDITIONAL
INFORMATION

ONE

TERMS AND DEFINITIONS USED IN THIS BOOK

Listed below are some of the terms used in this book. The terms are listed to increase understanding of the stories and suggestions in this book, but are not a comprehensive list of diabetic medical terms.

Alpha-Glucosidase Inhibitors—A type of pill that works on the intestines to slow the breakdown of carbohydrates. Used alone, this type of pill does not cause low blood sugar. It is taken with each meal.

Basal rate—The low-level steady release of fast-acting insulin by an insulin pump. Sometimes a pump is programmed for several basal rates, depending on the time of day.

Biguanides—A type of pill that works on the liver to prevent the liver from releasing too much glucose. It is best taken with meals.

Bolus—The insulin dose given, at the instruction of the pump user, by an insulin pump before a meal or to reduce high blood sugar levels.

Checkpoint Charlie—The place at the border between East Berlin and West Berlin where guards were stationed, and Berliners sought permission to cross from one side of the Berlin Wall to the other. It was dismantled in 1990, one year after the fall of the Berlin Wall.

Glucagon—An injectable preparation available by prescription to treat severe low blood sugar.

Glucose tablets—Manufactured products specifically made to treat low blood sugar. Manufacturers claim that glucose tablets are faster and more effective in treating low blood sugar than common remedies such as sugar or fruit juice.

Humalog—The rapid-acting insulin manufactured by Eli Lilly and Company. The generic name is lispro.

Intermediate-acting insulin—Insulin that begins working 2 to 4 hours after injection, peaks 4 to 12 hours later, and lasts for approximately 12 to 18 hours.

Ketoacidosis—A condition caused by lack of insulin or an increase in stress hormones. The condition is shown by high blood sugar levels and ketones (caused by a breakdown of body fat) in the urine.

Lantus insulin—The brand name for a long-acting insulin (glargine) manufactured by Aventis Pharmaceuticals, which has an onset of between 2 and 4 hours, and does not have any peaking time. Lantus must not be mixed with any other insulins and must not be taken intravenously.

Long-acting insulin—Insulin that reaches the bloodstream 6 to 10 hours after injection and is effective for 18 to 24 hours. However, Lantus (glargine) insulin reaches the bloodstream in less time. Other long-term insulins with effects similar to Lantus may be released in the near future.

Meglitinides—A type of pill that works on the pancreas to promote insulin production. This type of pill has the potential to cause low blood sugar levels and should only be taken with a meal. Brand names of this pill include Prandin and Starlix.

NPH insulin—The generic name for an intermediate-acting insulin.

Pills—There are 5 types of pills that treat type-2 diabetes: Alpha-Glucosidase Inhibitors; Biguanides; Meglitinides; Sulfonylureas; and Thuazikudubeduibes. For more information, see the definition for each type of pill and how it functions.

Pump, insulin—An insulin pump is a small computerized device that delivers insulin in steady basal doses and bolus doses. Doses are delivered through a plastic tube (catheter) inserted into the skin via a small needle that is taped in place. Pumps can release very small doses of insulin similar to a body's normal insulin release. Pumps do not monitor blood sugar levels, which must be done by the pump user.

Rapid-acting insulin—Insulin that begins working approximately 15 minutes after injection and works for 2 to 4 hours. In addition to Humalog, mentioned in some of the stories in this book, the rapid-acting insulin known as Novolog (insulin aspart) is manufactured by Novo Nordisk.

Regular insulin—The generic name for short-acting insulin.

Short-acting insulin—Insulin that begins working 30 minutes after injection, peaks 2 to 3 hours after injection, and is effective for a total of 3 to 6 hours.

Sulfonylureas—This type of pill works on the pancreas to promote insulin production. This type of pill can cause low blood sugar level and should only be taken with a meal. Some of the pills remain effective for more than 24 hours. There are many generic and brand names for this type of pill, including Amaryl,

Glucotrol XL, Diabeta, Micronase, Glynase, Tolinase, Ovinase, and Diabinese.

Thuazikudubeduibes (TZDs)—This type of pill works on muscle cells to cause the cells to be more sensitive to insulin. It takes 4 to 6 weeks to affect blood sugar levels.

Type-1 diabetes—Diabetes caused because the pancreas no longer makes insulin. Type-1 diabetics require insulin.

Type-2 diabetes—Diabetes caused by any one of several factors, including (i) a pancreas that does not make sufficient insulin, (ii) a liver that releases too much glucose, or (iii) muscle cells that do not easily take in glucose. A type-2 diabetic may be treated with insulin, pills only, diet only, or a combination of these.

CONVERSION FORMULAS

INSULIN AND SYRINGES

To use a U-100 syringe with U-40 insulin, you must take 2 1/2 times as much U-40 insulin to get your correct dose. For example: 10 units (of U-100 insulin) x 2.5 = 25 units of U-40 insulin (in a U-100 syringe).

To use a U-40 syringe with U-100 insulin, you must take only 40% of the measurement using a U-40 syringe. For example: if you take 20 units of U-100 insulin, the dose would be 20 units x 40% = 8 units of measurement in a U-40 syringe.

Note: If you purchase both U-40 insulin and U-40 insulin you do not have to use any of the above conversion formulas.

BLOOD SUGAR MEASUREMENTS

In many other countries, the system for measuring blood sugar levels is different than in the United States. If you use the other country's system, you must multiply by 18. For example, a blood sugar level of 6 (millimol/litre) in some other countries must be multiplied by 18 to result in a blood sugar level of 108 (milligrams/decilitre) in U.S. measurements.

TEMPERATURE

To convert centigrade to Fahrenheit: Multiply by 1.8 and add 32.

To convert Fahrenheit to centigrade: Subtract 32 and multiply by 0.55.

BIBLIOGRAPHY AND ADDITIONAL INFORMATION

American Diabetes Association Complete Guide to Diabetes, 3rd Edition.
New York, NY: Bantam 2003.

Fitzhenry, Robert I. *The Harper Book of Quotations*, 3rd Edition. New York, NY: HarperCollins Publishers Inc. 1993.

Diabetes Forecast magazine, subscription to which is a benefit of membership in the American Diabetes Association, at 1-800-806-7801; wwww.diabetes.org.

Diabetes Health magazine, available by subscription at 1-800-488-8468; www.diabeteshealth.com.

INDEX

INDEX

ACKNOWLEDGMENTS

This book would not have been possible without the help of many people whom I would like to thank, including, Albert Ramos for his perceptive input and hard work; Eileen Brown and Colleen Dunn Bates for constant encouragement and many leads; Eleanor Brewer, Joanne Hodapp and Larry Hebegger for editorial suggestions; Lucas Barron, Briana Beltrán, Steven Cheng, Mirelle Day, Lea Hildebrand, Manuel Nuñez, Akemi Segawa, Libby Sewall and Fannie Tsui for language translations; Dr. Isabelle Runkle De La Vega, attending physician in Endocrinology at the Universidad Complutense de Madrid Hospital Clinico and associate professor at the Universidad Autónoma de Madrid in Madrid, Spain; Dr. Roger Lerner; Dr. Louis Acosta, Mike Acosta, Marco Beltrán, Cathy Elliot, Denise Little and Sherry Neil-Urban, for sharing their stories; Stefan Gutermuth for his graphic design work; Liz Kee for her illustrations; my husband, Arnoldo Beltrán, for being the best travel organizer and guide; and, last but not least, my daughter, Briana Beltrán, for being a great navigator and language translator on all our trips together.

About the Authors and Contributors

MARILYN GARCIA practices law in Los Angeles, California, and lives with her family in Pasadena, California. She has traveled to Mexico, Costa Rica, China, Hong Kong, Taiwan, Morocco, Turkey, and many countries in Europe, including Andorra. She received a B.A. from Stanford University and a J.D. from The Yale Law School.

DENISE LITTLE is a writer and executive editor at Tekno Books, in Green Bay, Wisconsin. She has been a bookstore manager, the founder and first president of a large writer's chapter, and the national buyer of romance, science fiction, and fantasy for Barnes & Noble.

DR. LOUIS ACOSTA is the Chief of Staff at Queen of Angels Hospital in Los Angeles, California.

MIKE ACOSTA is Vice President Quality /Regulatory, for a multinational medical device company, and lives with his family in Northern California.

CATHERINE ELLIOT is a computer artist who lives in Los Angeles, California.

SHERRY NEIL-URBAN teaches nursing students at a community college in Carson, City, Nevada, and lives with her family in Reno, Nevada.

ELIZABETH KEE is a student at New York University.